DIRECT DRILLING AND
REDUCED CULTIVATIONS

DIRECT DRILLING AND REDUCED CULTIVATIONS

H. P. ALLEN B.Sc., Ph.D. (Dunelm)

FARMING PRESS LIMITED

Wharfedale Road, Ipswich, Suffolk

First published 1981

ISBN 0 75236 113 0

Photoset, printed and bound in Great Britain by
Redwood Burn Limited, Trowbridge, Wiltshire

Contents

Illustrations

* colour plates.

Foreword

by PROFESSOR E. W. RUSSELL CMG

British agriculture is having to adapt to a high wage economy with a consequent decrease in the labour force and this adaptation has proceeded very rapidly on the arable farms. The change has been most noticeable during the corn harvest, for the combine harvester has taken over completely from the old binder and men and women stooking in the harvest fields. But after harvest one still commonly sees the land being prepared for the next crop by methods that are in essence those that have been in use for the last two centuries, based on the use of ploughs, cultivators, harrows and rolls, the only difference being that the small horse-drawn implements have been replaced by much larger tractor-drawn ones. These traditional methods of cultivation are power- and often time-demanding, for there is usually an appreciable time gap between the successive operations; so at the same time they are labour demanding during this period and also very dependent on the weather.

Farmers, implement manufacturers and research workers have tried, for many years, to develop methods for making the transition from stubble to seedbed as independent of the weather as possible, and have therefore put much work into the essential requirements of an acceptable seedbed. Trials at Rothamsted about fifty years ago indicated that the most important requirement for any system of seedbed preparation was efficient weed control, and that if the land was clean and nearly weed-free crops were not very sensitive to seedbed tilth. Thus this early work demonstrated the importance of judging seedbed cultivation operations by their efficiency in controlling weeds in the seedbed and whilst the crop was still young; but it was not further developed to discover what were the minimum requirements for a seedbed to give an acceptable plant stand.

The introduction of herbicides nearly forty years ago began a revolution in crop management. The early herbicides were selective and were used principally in growing cereals to suppress a wide range of broad-leaved weeds, with a consequent great improve-

11

ment in the cleanness of the fields, ease of harvesting and often increased yields; but they had little effect on the sequence of cultivations for seedbed preparation. However the introduction of the bipyridyl herbicides paraquat and diquat by ICI opened up the possibility of a revolution in cultivation techniques because these herbicides killed a very wide range of weeds when sprayed on them at a suitable time, leaving the land temporarily weed-free. Consequently the Plant Protection Division of ICI began a series of experiments designed to test the revolutionary possibility of omitting all cultivations and drilling cereals directly into weed-free stubbles. These showed that under suitable conditions cereal yields, and particularly winter cereal yields, could be at least as high under these direct drilling practices as under traditional techniques.

These techniques were rapidly taken up by a number of farmers and were introduced into the research programmes of both the agricultural advisory services and the research stations to discover the conditions under which they could be recommended to farmers. This book describes the results of this work. It details the various conditions under which it is likely to be profitable and the various factors limiting the more general acceptance of these new techniques, and gives the experiences of several farmers who are at present using them. The book also emphasises that it is not a technique restricted to cereal growing but has great relevance to the growing of forage crops, particularly fast-growing brassica crops such as rape and turnips, and the reseeding of grasslands.

Direct Drilling and Reduced Cultivations also stresses that the adoption of some of these techniques can have major consequences for farm management. They require the development of seed drills specially designed to penetrate the surface of uncultivated soils, if possible when last season's stubble is still present, and these may have to prepare a narrow band of loosened soil into which the seed can be drilled. They require a high level of management by the farmer but they may also ease many problems of such management. The soil remains more compact and stronger and is therefore better able to withstand trampling by livestock and compaction by implements; but the harmful effect of compaction is to some extent counteracted by the conservation of the continuity of soil cracks and root channels from the surface into the subsoil and the greater earthworm activity found when direct drilling is used. The techniques may also affect the optimum level of fertiliser (particularly nitrogen fertiliser), the incidence of plant pests (particularly slugs in the seedbed), plant diseases and the time of sowing. Their use also demands the need for a complete stubble burn, for in wet years bits of straw on or in the soil surface at drilling time may get pushed into the drill slit and cause very poor germination due to the production of plant toxins.

This book comes at a very timely moment, for the period of rapid developments of these techniques is now probably over and the principal task now is to encourage their acceptance in practice. This book should be a great stimulus to this development.

E. W. RUSSELL

Acknowledgements

I wish to acknowledge, with grateful thanks, my indebtedness to the following for reading chapters, allowing me to use and quote the results of experiments and development work, and supplying photographs and diagrams:

Ministry of Agriculture, Fisheries and Food—Agricultural Development and Advisory Service.
Eastern Region. Dr D. B. Davies, Mr K. R. Hubbard, Mr J. M. Procter, Mr J. B. Finney, Mr W. D. Theophilus

Drayton Experimental Husbandry Farm—Mr J. M. Oliphant
High Mowthorpe Experimental Husbandry Farm—Mr D. A. Perks
Redesdale Experimental Husbandry Farm—Mr J. R. Thompson

Agricultural Research Council.
Letcombe Laboratory—Mr J. Lake, Dr R. Q. Cannell, Dr F. B. Ellis
Weed Research Oganisation—Mr J. G. Elliott

Norfolk Agricultural Station—Mr S. P. McClean, Mr M. Nuttall

National Institute of Agricultural Engineering—Mr D. E. Patterson

Scottish Institute of Agricultural Engineering—Dr Brennan Soane

ICI—Plant Protection Division
Messrs J. N. Page, G. A. Harris, A. Bloomfield, J. D. Pidgeon, M. A. Gowman, N. Catlin, K. G. Hughes, B. W. Cox, Miss Jean Elsie, Miss Grace Gillard, Miss Jill Chuter, Mr. R. Jeater

ICI—Agricultural Division: Mr. A. E. M. Hood

Farmers
Messrs R. H. Jenkinson, R. Holbrook, M. Bendall, J. Muirhead, Strutt and Parker Farms Ltd, Mr. A. Forsyth

My thanks also to Mrs Marjorie Long Fox, Mrs Barbara Sidwell and to my daughter, Mrs Rosemary Newton, for typing the manuscript.

Chapter 1
INTRODUCTION

Until very recently, in fact up to the outbreak of the Second World War, the need to plough and cultivate the soil in preparation for the sowing or planting of crops was never seriously questioned. Indeed, attempts by those more imaginative scientists and cultivators to grow crops without this careful preparation often came to grief, thus reinforcing the view of the more orthodox-minded majority that the absence of ploughing was, *in itself,* the cause of failure.

In 1975 in a paper given at Reading, Sir Charles Pereira, then Chief Scientist to the Ministry of Agriculture, Fisheries & Food, stated that 'the most logical approach to tillage should start from the observation that, when free of Man's interference, most of the earth's soils are clothed with a vigorous system of vegetation which requires no uniform seedbeds'. He urged that 'we should look more carefully at the mechanism by which soils and their plant cover interact to provide a tilth in which seeds are germinated and plants established without any expenditure of applied horse-power'.[4]

When our early forebears learned how to tame and domesticate the dog and horse, this in turn enabled them to hunt and capture other animals, and to tame the cow, sheep, goat and pig from which they learned to gain and use the milk, flesh, hides and wool. These new acquisitions meant, however, that men had to become less nomadic and to acquire the skills of providing more efficiently for themselves, their families and their herds and flocks. It is said that in those far-off days when they buried their dead, they buried also 'food for the journey' in the newly dug earth and they found that the seeds (which would include the grass precursors of our present-day cereals) developed into plants bearing many times the number of seeds buried. So they cleared more ground, put in more seed and were amazed and pleased to find that they reaped a similar dividend when plants grew and matured. They may well have noted 'the abundance of vegetation with which Nature clothed the earth,'

17

but they noted also that to grow what they wanted when they wanted it, they needed to clear ground, to dig it and plant the seed into the dug soil.[3]

In the course of time the first ploughs were fashioned and these were steadily improved throughout the centuries. The astonishing thing is that although the art of tillage was discovered thousands of years ago, until the middle of the eighteenth century the plough, designed originally to be drawn by an eight-ox team, remained the only horse-drawn implement capable of loosening the top four inches of soil. Thus, not surprisingly, the necessity of ploughing as a first operation was never questioned.

In the eighteenth century Jethro Tull realised the importance of weeds in competition with crop plants. His system of wide-spaced drilling of crops and interrow horse-hoeing allowed for the first time the means of effective weed control in the growing crop. In spite of this, primary cultivations were never studied, nor was their role examined. Their need was just assumed and in the nineteenth century came the development of a wide range of cultivating implements to supplement the mouldboard plough. The implements themselves and the ploughs were constantly improved.

Thus with these newer ploughs, cultivators, discs and tined harrows, allied with an ample labour force, the tradition of ploughing and cultivation to produce a seedbed continued unquestioned. This was not because farmers were incurious, but because they had no strong reasons to ask these particular questions. Furthermore, cultivation was (and is still) considered an art, and there was little or no quantitative knowledge of what cultivations accomplished.

It was taken for granted that ploughing relieved soil compaction, aerated soil, improved drainage, and buried weeds; that is, that it was an essential primary cultivation. With orthodox rotational farming, which was a common feature of United Kingdom agriculture in the relatively recent past, the deleterious effects of ploughing in unsuitable conditions, and excessive and untimely cultivation—which became so evident with the more intensive farming in the 1950s and 1960s—were not apparent. Reassessment of cultivation systems by farmers came much later and only as a result of such factors as a steadily diminishing (but increasingly expensive) labour force, a steady rise in machinery costs, and the development of herbicides first to control broad-leaved weeds and later to suppress grass weeds.

Russell[5] carried out a series of experiments at Rothamsted (on heavy land) and Woburn (on light sand) between 1930 and 1939. These experiments indicated that, *provided weed competition was removed,* yields of wheat, barley and mangolds were the same on land which was only cultivated as on land which was ploughed *and* cultivated. Yields on the 'no-plough' plots were depressed, however, if the particular cultivation treatment left a weedy seedbed. In other words, in the fields in which the experiments were conducted ploughing was superior *only* where it produced the better weed control. These experiments were described by Professor Russell in 1945 at a meeting of the Institute of British Agricultural Engineers.

Little progress was made with non-ploughing techniques, however, in spite of the rapid development of herbicides throughout the 1950s. There were two probable reasons for this: first, the new herbicides remained active in the soil some time after their application, thus posing a threat to any seeds drilled into soil recently treated; and second, there was still insufficient motivation to develop alternatives to ploughing. Things were changing but the 'cereal boom' had not yet arrived and it seemed that traditional cultivation systems still met farmers' needs satisfactorily. The 'trigger' which set off research into chemically-assisted minimal tillage and direct drilling techniques was the discovery of the bipyridyls at the end of the 1950s by ICI.[1] Even then the idea remained a research theme viewed with some scepticism and not a little amusement in farming circles, and it was not until much later in the 1960s that the economic and agronomic possibilities of these new techniques led to extensive field development.

Examination of newer, more streamlined systems of cultivation was encouraged by the fact that in the 1960s and early 1970s the labour force on farms fell by 47 per cent, the minimum wage for an adult man rose by 38 per cent, and further, between 1975 and 1977, the costs of running a tractor trebled.[2] Developing concurrently with this interest in chemically assisted minimal tillage, however, was a move towards the use of high-horsepower tractors and heavy, expensive cultivating tackle. Indeed, these two contrasting methods of speeding up cultivations and seedbed preparation arose from the intensification of cereal growing and its transformation into a high-input, high-output enterprise where the aim was to grow as large a target area of cereals, especially winter cereals, as possible.

The aims of power cultivations and minimal tillage were similar, i.e. to replace the mouldboard plough, but their approaches were fundamentally different. Minimal tillage was seeking to minimise the frequency and depth of cultivation, and even (with direct drilling) to eliminate cultivation. On the other hand the 'high power approach' involved very considerable cultivation of the soil, and it is regrettable, but true, that even as recently as the 1960s one important aspect of farming which was at best taken for granted and at worst treated with near contempt was soil management. Too often cropping enterprises were intensified *at the expense* of the farmer's basic asset—the soil.

The essence of good soil management may be defined as the ability to select those cultivation systems which will maintain the particular soil conditions where the optimal crop growth may be achieved (other inputs assumed), coupled with the selection of the most suitable crops for each soil type. The advent of the idea of minimal tillage focused attention on this key factor.

THE CONCEPT OF CHEMICALLY-ASSISTED MINIMAL TILLAGE

The terms used in this book are defined below. Some may argue with the definitions, but at least the reader will know what the author has in mind.

No-plough cultivations **Alternative cultivations**	*Any* method of sowing a crop *without* using the mouldboard plough (with or without the use of a herbicide to kill stubble weeds or grass sward).
Reduced cultivations **Minimal tillage**	As above, but where the cultivations are few and shallow.
Direct drilling	Drilling a crop into stubble or sward, usually killed by a herbicide, without *any* cultivation save possibly for the production of a 'scratch-tilth'.

Chemically assisted minimal tillage had been investigated in the United States, New Zealand and Scotland prior to the advent of paraquat. However, the herbicides employed (mainly dalapon and amino-triazole) were residually active in the soil—which meant a long delay before seeds could be sown.

When ICI first considered the prospect of investigating paraquat-assisted direct drilling in 1961 they faced two major problems. First, there were many unknowns about the basic idea; and, second, motivations for using the technique could only be the subject of guesswork. The thinking was 'we have a herbicide which will kill all green vegetation (i.e. all green aerial growth) and which becomes inactivated very rapidly upon contact with the soil. Can we use these two properties to develop techniques for destroying vegetation and then planting crops immediately afterwards, with minimal (or even without any) disturbance of the top soil?' First, the assumption was made that paraquat-assisted direct drilling was a feasible proposition. Second, the potential benefits that such a technique might confer (or at any rate those that could be perceived) were enumerated. Third, an attempt was made to anticipate as far as possible the questions which would have to be answered before direct drilling could be recommended without reservation. The assumption, the potential benefits and the questions are set out below, and the work that has been and is being done in an attempt to answer the questions forms the main subject of this book.

Assumption—that it is possible to destroy stubble vegetation, an old pasture or a ley sward with a chemical which is rapidly inactivated on contact with the soil, and to sow the seeds of a new crop immediately afterwards without any cultivation of the topsoil and without detriment to the growth development and ultimate yield of that crop.

POTENTIAL BENEFITS

1. With such a streamlined operation it should be possible:
● to save time on the land (especially important as weather conditions begin to deteriorate in the autumn);
● to save labour;
● to save fuel;
● to plant the optimal 'target' area of the crop in the time available;
● to save money.
2. Minimising moisture loss in situations where surface moisture is critical.
3. Retaining organic matter in the top 5 cm of soil.
4. Reducing the risk of soil erosion by rain or by wind.
5. Retaining the basic advantages of an undisturbed topsoil (good vertical communication from topsoil to subsoil via cracks, old root and earthworm channels, thus permitting good drainage.)
6. By maintaining surface consolidation:

of the rate of deterioration, for instance in long runs of cereals).
6. By maintaining surface consolidation:
● with new grass, to permit early grazing;
● with forage crops, e.g. kale, to permit 'in situ' feeding (with
    reduced risk of 'poaching').
7. Particularly overseas, to allow double cropping or three crops in
    two years by streamlining planting techniques.

QUESTIONS

At the start of the work there were a daunting number of 'unknowns' not all of which were even listed by those planning the
experiments; many were thrown up as problems encountered by
the experimenters themselves.

1. Are all soils suitable—if not, what are the prerequisites for suc-
    cessful drilling?
2. Would seed rates have to be increased?
3. Would it be possible to direct drill seed and fertiliser together
    without detriment?
4. Would uptake of nutrients, N P & K especially, be affected by
    direct drilling?
5. What would be the effect on weeds, diseases and pests?
6. Would root development be affected adversely?
7. What about straw—is its removal essential; should it be
    chopped and spread, or should it be burnt?
8. Would yields be affected adversely?
9. What would be the effect of repeated direct drilling over a
    period of years, assuming this to be agronomically feasible?
10. Of major importance, what type or types of seed drill would be
    required to achieve satisfactory sowing of crop seed into uncul-
    tivated soil?

In the chapters which follow, the results of research and development work since the early 1960s are described on a crop by crop
basis. Greatest emphasis is placed on the cereal crop because most
of the more fundamental studies were centred around cereals,
whilst the results of such work applied basically to direct drilling,
irrespective of crop. For each of the crops covered the fruits of research and development are summarised and woven into guidelines for adoption of the technique. The development of suitable
machinery is described in detail as are the economics of direct drilling; case studies of long-term practitioners of the new techniques
are presented, and major developments of direct drilling overseas
are reviewed.

REFERENCES

1. BOON, W. R. (1966), *New Scientist,* 1966, **30** (44), 310–11.
2. BULLEN, E. F. (1977), *Span,* **20**, 53.
3. ORR, J. (1922), *A Short History of British Agriculture,* Oxford Univ. Press, 7–9.
4. PEREIRA, H. C. (1975), *Outl. Agric.,* **8** (Special No.), 211–12.
5. RUSSELL, E. W. (1945), *Proc. Inst. Brit. Agric. Engrs.,* III (7), 99–111.

Chapter 2

FIELD EXPERIMENTS 1961–74

EARLY TRIALS

The first significant experiments with chemically assisted minimal tillage in the United Kingdom were conducted at the Grassland Research Institute at Hurley near Reading, Berkshire[2] and at ICI's Jealott's Hill Research Station, near Bracknell, Berkshire[5] starting in the autumn of 1961. Both projects involved winter wheat and both concerned minimal tillage and direct drilling treatments applied to grassland.

Experiment at the Grassland Research Institute

Arnott and Clement set out with three objectives.

1. To investigate the possibility of growing wheat after a ley without ploughing (i.e. in a situation where organic matter and crumb stability under grass are confined to the top 2 inches of soil).
2. To study the effect of compaction of soils under leys on the growth of winter wheat.
3. To compare the level of nitrogen release on ploughed soil with that on soil destroyed by herbicides.

Three treatments were involved:

- Ploughing and cultivating.
- Destruction of the sward with 10 lb/acre of amino-triazole + ammonium thiocyanate activator.
- Skimming off the grass just below the soil surface with a flail-type forage harvester.

Six sowing dates were compared: 29, 30 September, 3, 10 October, 8, 12 November, 1961. No fertiliser was applied.

The main indications from the experiment were as follows:

1. The herbicide killed the ley slowly but completely.

2. Residual toxicity reduced the numbers of wheat seedlings *only* in the first and second sowings after the applications of amino-triazole.
3. Skimming reduced competition from the old sward until the spring of 1962, but thereafter the old grass recovered with adverse effects on the wheat crop.
4. There was no significant difference in yield between treatments save that, for some reason not explained, yields from the third sowing were significantly higher after spraying than after ploughing.
5. There was no evidence from this experiment that yields on the plots not ploughed were limited either by soil compaction or by reduced mineralisation of nitrogen.

Experiment at Jealott's Hill.
The site selected for the Jealott's Hill Experiment (named CPI) was an old but well-managed, ryegrass dominant, permanent sward. Hybrid 46 winter wheat was the test crop and there were three treatments:

1. Sprayed with paraquat at 3 lb ion/acre (12 pints/acre or 17 litres/ha of the commercial product) and direct drilled with an Australian drill, the Jefferies 'Grasslands' sod seeder.
2. Sprayed as in 1, ploughed, cultivated and sown.
3. Traditional, i.e. ploughed, cultivated and sown.

No nitrogen was applied to the seedbed but three levels of top dressing were applied in the spring of 1962: 0, 60, and 90 units per acre. Yields are shown in Table 1.

Table 1. Winter Wheat yields, 1961 (adjusted to 85% D/M)

Treatment	Yield of grain (cwt/acre)
Sprayed and direct drilled	55·4
Sprayed, ploughed and drilled	60·7
Ploughed and drilled	58·3
Sig. diff. $(P = 0·05) = 2·9$	

(Source: After Hood et al., 1963) (Ref. 5)

Whilst the yield of wheat on the direct drilled treatment was significantly *lower* than on the other two treatments (see Table 1), it was nonetheless satisfactory, even with the totally inappropriate seeder which was used.

In this experiment there was no response to fertiliser, but in a trial with 'Jufy' spring wheat drilled into a timothy–meadow fescue–white clover ley, where spraying paraquat and direct drilling (one day afterwards and twenty-two days later) was compared with ploughing and traditional seedbed preparation, there was a considerable response to seedbed fertiliser (see Table 2).

Table 2. Yields of 'Jufy' spring wheat (adjusted to 85% D/M) (cwt/acre)

| Treatment | Units N per acre | | |
	0	60	90
Sprayed and direct drilled—February	18·7	28·9	31·4
Sprayed and direct drilled—March	17·2	26·8	26·2
Ploughed, cultivated and drilled	27·8	33·0	29·8
Sig. diff. (P = 0·05) = 2·0			

(Source: After Hood et al., 1963) (Ref. 5)

Direct drilling proved markedly inferior to traditional methods where no seedbed nitrogen was applied, but at 90 units of nitrogen the plots direct drilled in February out-yielded the ploughed plots although not significantly. This phenomenon of continuing response of direct drilled cereals to increasing levels of nitrogen has been noted in many experiments and will be discussed later.

The population of wheat seedlings on the direct drilled plots was only 60 per cent of that on the ploughed plots due to slugs, and on large areas of the direct drilled treatment there was strong regrowth of couch grass (*Agropyron repens*) which competed seriously with the crop; this was most evident in the 'no nitrogen' plots. The combined assault of slugs and couch grass no doubt accounted for a substantial proportion of the yield loss on those plots.

The winter wheat experiment at Jealott's Hill described above (CP1) was destined to continue for seven years and will be referred to again shortly. In 1963 a winter wheat experiment was carried out on poorly drained rye-grass-dominant pasture, also at Jealott's Hill, and involving the same treatment comparisons as were used in the 1961 trial. In this case the direct drilled plots were badly waterlogged, whereas the ploughed plots were hardly affected. There was also marked regeneration of meadow foxtail (*Alopecurus pratensis*), creeping bent (*Agrostis stolonifera*) and couch grass on both plots. The soil was loam overlying London clay and the plots were drilled on 31 October 1963 (see Table 3).[6]

Two points were becoming clear. First, in conditions where there

Table 3. Yields of winter wheat, 1963 (adjusted to 85% D/M) (cwt/acre)

Units N per acre	Sprayed & direct drilled	Sprayed, ploughed, cultivated & drilled	Ploughed, cultivated & drilled
0	10·9	21·4	19·5
75	13·6	29·8	32·9
100	18·0	35·0	35·5
	SE (single sub-plot ± 6·2)		
	Sig. diffs. N rate means—6·3		
	(P = 0·05) Cultivation means—4·8		

(Source: After Hood et al., *Nature*, 1964) (Ref. 6)

was considerable surface water, the water tended to remain on the surface of direct drilled plots and to move away in the ploughed plots. Second, the poor crop on the direct drilled plots was not able to offer serious competition to those weed grasses well able to withstand waterlogging.

By 1964 a pattern was beginning to emerge from the long-term winter wheat experiment initiated in the autumn of 1961 (CP1). The same treatments were repeated on the same plots in the autumns of 1962 and 1963, and Table 4 shows the results of the first three years of the trial.[7]

Table 4. (Experiment CP1) Effect of pre-sowing techniques on grain yields of winter wheat (yields in cwt/acre—adjusted to 85% D/M)

Treatment	1962	1963	1964	Mean
Sprayed and direct drilled	55·4	58·9	40·3	49·5
Sprayed, ploughed, cultivated and drilled	60·7	53·0	35·2	49·6
Ploughed, cultivated and drilled	58·3	52·2	37·1	49·2
Sig. diff (P = 0·05) 2·9		n.s.	n.s.	

(Source: After Hood et al., 7th BWCC 1964) (Ref. 7)

It will be seen that direct drilling held its own in the second and third years—in fact in 1964 yields on direct drilled plots were superior to those on the other two treatments, though not significantly so. This experiment continued to give confidence that a workable and successful direct drilling technique would be fashioned eventually.

The ICI experimental programme, both at Jealott's Hill and at outside centres, was expanded between 1963 and 1966,[6,8,9,10] and several aspects studied, in particular:

- Comparison of rates of paraquat.
- Timing of application of paraquat.
- Response to nitrogen.
- Effect of timing of application of nitrogen on yields of winter wheat.
- Single versus split applications of nitrogen on winter wheat.
- Comparison of seed rates.
- Comparison of combine drilling with drilling grain and broadcasting fertiliser, in a direct drilling system.
- Effect of time of drilling on yield of direct drilled spring barley.

Comparison of rates of paraquat
When averaged over time of application, yields after spraying with 2 lb ion/acre of paraquat (8 pints/acre or 11·2 litres/ha of 'Gramoxone') were significantly higher than after 1 lb ion/acre. Clearly this reflected the type and density of the stubble weed population in these particular trials.

Timing of application of paraquat
The timing of spraying within the three-week period up to and including the day of direct drilling did not influence yield of winter wheat. With spring barley, however, December spraying produced results from direct drilling similar to those from ploughing, whereas February spraying produced poorer yields from direct drilling.

Response to nitrogen
In the winter wheat experiments there was very little response to autumn-applied (i.e. seedbed) nitrogen, but direct drilled crop yields increased with increasing levels of nitrogen top dressing up to 120 units per acre. With spring barley there was increasing response to increased nitrogen and at 75 units of N yields on direct drilled plots were equal and, at 100 units, superior to those on ploughed plots.

Timing of nitrogen application
Winter wheat—Single Application. Five times of application were compared: 28 October 1965, 7 and 28 March 1966, 21 April 1966 and 12 May 1966, and highest yields followed the March applications, especially the late March treatment (see Table 5).

With split applications the four systems compared gave similar yields. Results are shown in Table 5.

Two outside trials on winter wheat (where only times of *single*

Table 5. Direct drilled winter wheat—timing of spring nitrogen top dressing (yields in cwt/acre—adjusted to 85% D/M)

Control (No nitrogen)	Dates of application (single)				
	28.10.65	7.3.66	28.3.66	21.4.66	12.5.66
	33·1	42·7	43·4	40·7	38·2
	(split)				
29·8	14.2.66 & 21.4.66 42·7	14.2.66 & 12.5.66 41·2	7.3.66 & 21.4.66 42·8	7.3.66 & 12.5.66 42·9	
		SE = ± 2·26 (73 d.f.)			

(Source: Jeater, 8th BWCC 1966) (Ref. 10)

applications were compared) showed similar trends, March application giving better yields than April or May dressings.

Comparison of seed rates
Results are shown in Table 6, and are very much in line with those expected from similar drilling rates of conventionally sown winter wheat.

Table 6. Direct drilled winter wheat—comparison of seed rates (yields in cwt/acre adjusted to 85% D/M)

Seed rate (cwt/acre)	Mean number of plants established per yard of row	Yield
1·5	40	33·1
2·0	53	38·4
2·5	65	35·2
	SE = ± 3·05 (9 d.f.)	

(Source: Jeater, 8th BWCC 1966) (Ref. 10)

Combine-drilling versus broadcasting
The results of two experiments conducted at Jealott's Hill are given in Table 7.

Two inferences may be drawn from these results. First, although there was a general trend towards slightly higher yields on combined drilled plots (whether ploughed or direct drilled), these differences were not significant; and second, direct drilled yields were at least the equal of those on the ploughed treatments.

Table 7. Spring barley—comparison of combine-drilling and broadcasting fertiliser (yields in cwt/acre adjusted to 85% D/M)

Trial No.	Rate of compound fertiliser (22:11:11) cwt/acre	Direct Drilled		Ploughed	
		Combine drilled	Broadcast	Combine drilled	Broadcast
1	3·0	36·5	34·5	36·0	32·7
	4·5	37·9	37·1	37·2	36·8
2	3·0	38·3	41·2	38·3	35·0
	4·5	46·7	45·4	45·8	44·9

SE Trial No 1 ± 2·6 (21 d.f.)
Trial No 2 ± 1·65 (21 d.f.)

(Source: Jeater, 8th BWCC 1966) (Ref. 10)

Effect of time of drilling on yields of spring barley

In this particular trial there was marked advantage in February drilling of spring barley (see Table 8). This would be expected, provided measures are taken to protect the early drilled barley against leaf blotch (*Rhynchosporium secale*). Note also that barley direct drilled in April, though yielding much less when no nitrogen was applied, gave yields more or less equal with those from ploughing at 50 and 75 units of nitrogen per acre, and exceeded the yields from ploughing at the highest level of nitrogen.

Table 8. Spring barley—effect of time of drilling (yields in cwt/acre adjusted to 85% D/M)

Units N per acre	Direct Drilled		Ploughed April
	February	April	
0	36·6	32·2	40·9
50	47·1	41·1	42·6
75	49·3	40·2	41·5
100	48·7	39·1	37·8

SE (columns) ± 0·95 (27 d.f.)
(other comparisons) ± 1·17 (9 d.f.)

(Source: Jeater, 8th BWCC 1966) (Ref. 10)

An important practical point brought out in the experiment was that by direct drilling on Jealott's Hill soils (loams overlying

London clay), it is possible to plant spring barley two months earlier than following ploughing—February ploughing is not a practical proposition.

Experiment CP1, Jealott's Hill 1961–9—Summary
Details of the result of this experiment over the full eight years of its duration are displayed in Table 9.

Reference has already been made to the yields achieved by the three cultivation systems in the years 1962–4 inclusive. Direct drilling gave highest yields in 1965, and in 1966, 1967 and 1968, at spring N rates of 80 and 120 units per acre direct drilling and ploughing produced comparable yields. At lower rates of N direct drilling gave poorer yields, due largely to a heavy infestation of meadow foxtail (*Alopecurus pratensis*) which gained ground year by year. Onion couch (*Arrhenatherum elatius* var. *bulbosum*) also invaded the direct drilled plots. Attempts were made to suppress these grass weeds by increasing the dosage rates of paraquat and in 1969 by introducing a second application, but without success, and it became necessary to terminate the experiment after the 1969 harvest.

Take-all increased in all treatments from 1964 onwards until 1969, much less so in direct drilled plots, however. In 1969 levels of infestation were very low in all treatments. *Cephalosporium* leaf stripe depressed yields in 1966 and 1967 especially on the direct drilled treatments. Eyespot built up over the latter years of the experiment and reached similarly high levels in both direct and conventionally drilled plots in 1968 causing serious lodging.

Over its eight-year life CP1 delivered a considerable amount of most valuable information, and served its purpose well.

Experiments at NAAS (now ADAS) Experimental Husbandry Farms
In 1964 the Advisory arm of MAAF (then NAAS, now ADAS) started a series of experiments which were to continue until 1968. Participating EHFs were Boxworth near Huntingdon on boulder clay; Gleadthorpe, Notts. on light sand; Bridgets, Hampshire on chalk; High Mowthorpe, N. Yorkshire, on chalky silty loam over clay; and Rosemaund, Hereford on heavy red sandstone (well-drained loam).

Though there were variations in detail between EHF experiments, three major treatments were compared:

1. Ploughing and cultivating.

Table 9. Grain yields (cwt/acre) and incidence of foot-rot diseases: Experiment CP1

Harvest year and variety	'Gramoxone' pints/acre	Units/acre spring N	Yields averaged over N rates for 1st, 2nd, 3rd & 4th years — Sprayed and direct drilled	Sprayed, ploughed, cultivated & drilled	Ploughed, cultivated and drilled	Take-all — Sprayed and direct drilled	Take-all — Ploughed, cultivated and drilled	Eyespot — Sprayed and direct drilled	Eyespot — Ploughed, cultivated and drilled
1962 Hybrid 46	12	0	55·4	60·7	58·3	—	—	—	—
		30							
		50							
		70							
1963 Hybrid 46	12	0	52·9	53·0	52·2	—	—	—	—
		50							
		75							
		100							
1964 Hybrid 46	8	0	40·5	35·2	37·1	3	20	27	38
		40							
		80							
		120							
1965 Cappelle	4	0	36·0	29·4	26·3	14	64	26	17
		40							
		80							
		120							
1966 Cappelle	4	0	24·3	34·0	31·0	24	48	49	64
		40	34·2	39·9	41·0				
		80	37·8	39·4	38·1				
		120	35·5	33·6	35·8				
1967 Cappelle	4*	0	17·9	27·0	26·2	35	71	88	94
		40	27·4	35·8	33·8				
		80	31·0	41·4	35·7				
		120	32·1	36·9	32·9				
1968 Cappelle	4†	0	15·9	14·5	23·2	42	76		>95
		40	23·2	29·9	29·1				
		80	27·3	26·3	28·9				
		120	25·8	20·6	23·4				
1969 Cappelle	4‡	0	—	27·6	26·5	Very low	Very low	Very low	Very low
		40	—	46·8	39·7				
		80	39·4	55·0	49·8				
		120	50·9	58·4	54·4				

* 12 pints/acre on direct drilled plots   † 8 pints/acre on direct drilled plots   ‡ Direct drilled plots sprayed twice at 4 pints/acre, i.e. 25.9.68 and 7.10.68.   (Source: ICI Jealott's Hill Farm Guides 1969 & 1970)

2. One pass with a rotary cultivator (no pre-drilling herbicide).
3. Direct drilling following spraying with paraquat.

In an article reviewing this work in general terms at the completion of its second year, Whybrew[12] pointed out that ploughing, by definition, creates a situation in which the soil *has* to be cultivated extensively to produce a seedbed, and this may mean a delay of four to six weeks between ploughing and drilling, certainly on the heavier soils. With the availability of herbicides such as paraquat, the time was ripe to look at possible alternatives to ploughing.

Bullen,[3] then Director of Boxworth EHF, describing an early experiment with direct drilling on that farm, stated that as ploughing involved moving 1000 cubic yards of soil for every acre ploughed to a depth of 9 inches it was a costly process and any potential alternative merited close study. Bullen also took up Russell's earlier point, referring to a series of experiments in ploughing depth undertaken in the 1950s in some EHFs. They showed that, for cereals at least, similar yields were obtained from seedbeds prepared by cultivation and harrowing, as from ploughing and harrowing. Thus the *need* always to plough was challenged and now (i.e. 1964) the means of challenging the plough were at hand.

Bullen listed the potential advantages of direct drilling if it could be made to work:

● The prospect of eliminating the four-week delay after ploughing soil, necessary to allow the furrow slice to weather.
● The prospect of less need for expensive crawler tractors.

At the same time, he cited a number of problems to be solved, including (1) the need for more reliable grass weed control, (2) the need to design suitable machinery for direct drilling, (3) the need to determine to what extent fertiliser requirement might differ with direct drilling.

The results of these experiments were varied. Bullen concluded from his 1964 experiment that the drills then available were not suitable for direct drilling, that seed rates may have to be increased when direct drilling cereals on heavy soils, that higher levels of nitrogen may be required for direct drilled cereals, and that drainage problems may be made worse. On the credit side he noted that concentration of crop residues of organic matter generally in the top 5 cm soil may lead, in the long run, to amelioration of the surface soil 'which will help to offset any structure problems which may be brought about by minimal cultivations'. As we shall see later, Bullen's criticisms of early drill designs were well-founded, but his apprehensions about seed rates, extra nitrogen, and drainage problems were not confirmed.

The general results from the EHFs experiments were described by Whybrew.[13] He reported the following:

- Few changes in soil structure were noted except on sandy loam at Gleadthorpe where a thin 'platy' layer developed 5 cm below the surface.
- The studies had suggested that direct drilled crops produced a shallower root system.
- Slugs in the direct drilled slots were the main pest and caused considerable damage. It was essential that the slots were closed after direct drilling; if necessary, by light harrowing.
- Rhizomatous weeds, such as couch grass were more serious in direct drilled crops.
- Nitrogen levels need to be no higher for direct drilled crops than for crops grown traditionally.
- Direct drilling offered a considerable potential for saving time and labour, giving the cereal grower a better chance of sowing at the optimum time and enabling him to spend the minimal time *on* the land (tractor hours per acre recorded in the EHF experiments and averaged out are displayed in Table 10).
- There was a pressing need for improvement in drill design.

Table 10. Tractor-hours recorded for different cultivation systems—EHF experiments

	Tractor hours per acre		
Soil Type	Conventional	Minimal	Direct drilled
Light soils	2·58	1·28	0·45
Heavy soils	5·90	2·35	0·54

(Source: Whybrew 1967) (Ref. 13)

The overall conclusion was 'direct drill where a weed-free condition and soil type allow, and change to conventional cultivation where grass weed problems and soil conditions dictate'.

Experience at Drayton Experimental Husbandry Farm (MAFF, ADAS) 1968–9

This report by Whybrew was published in 1967 by which time he had gone to Drayton EHF as Assistant Director to Mr Ralph Bee. Drayton lies on heavy Lias clay (Evesham Series) and the reduced cultivation system in practice on that farm is described in Chapter 8. The 1968 autumn was one of the wettest in recent times, and it posed special problems on Drayton soil, into which a considerable acreage of winter crops had to be sown. Whybrew[14] considered the pros and cons of ploughing in the light of the 1968 autumn and listed the following functions of ploughing:

1. amelioration of soil structure by breaking from the main mass a layer of soil 6–9 inches deep;
2. aeration;
3. assistance with drainage by creating fissures through which surplus water can drain away;
4. turning in farmyard manure;
5. breaking up grassland;
6. putting crop residues underground where breakdown can take place.

Whybrew's contention was that with the exception of farmyard manure (FYM) all other functions of the mouldboard plough can be taken over by other methods. He argued also that, under cereals, the value of FYM was small and that it was probably better to use FYM under potatoes in rotation.

Whybrew's point was that the very act of ploughing makes it necessary to cultivate to reduce the furrow slice to small fragments to form a seedbed. To prepare a traditional seedbed takes on average four operations, and to achieve a large target acreage of winter crop on Drayton clay in any autumn is a fairly heavy task. To do so in an autumn as wet as 1968 was indeed a tall order and events dictated the substitution of the mouldboard plough by reduced cultivations (chisel ploughs etc.) using paraquat for weed control in the stubble of the previous crop.

THE STATE OF THE ART—1969

After eight years of field studies involving direct drilling of various small-seeded crops, it was becoming possible to draw up a list of problems solved and a much larger list of questions posed but not answered. Progress with these new techniques for sowing grass, forage brassica crops and other crops will be discussed in later chapters. In the cereal crop, although direct drilling was still in the development stage, and relatively few specially designed drills were available, ICI produced guidelines for those wishing to test this new system; these guidelines reflected both the extent and limitations of the collective experience of those who had been involved in the field research and development work in the period 1961-9. At that time direct drilling of cereals was recommended only on light to medium free-draining soil which should be free of stones and perennial weeds, especially rhizomatous perennial grasses like couch. No advice was offered for direct drilling heavier soils.

REVIEW OF UK EXPERIMENT RESULTS AND THEIR IMPLICATIONS 1961-74

Field Experiments carried out in the United Kingdom by ICI and ADAS (NAAS) and by ARC up to and including the 1973 harvest were summarised by Davies & Cannell and by Allen in papers delivered to a symposium at Reading early in 1975. Davies & Cannell dealt with the results and their implications and Allen outlined ICI's work during that period.[4,1]

Davies and Cannell pointed out that in the experiments conducted before 1970, average yields of winter wheat and spring barley after direct drilling were less than after ploughing, but that in later experiments there was little yield difference compared with ploughing. Table 11 illustrates this point very clearly.

This, of course, is general comment. In specific situations results over a period were more consistently encouraging. For example the results on spring barley from the long-term ICI experiment at Warminster on a chalk loam (Icknield series) soil carried out in the early-mid 1970s showed direct drilling to be equal or slightly superior to ploughing in four years out of five (see Table 12).

It is suggested[4] that lack of experience and poorer performance of drills in early years probably imposed severe limitations on success, especially with direct drilling, and other evidence is adduced (frequency of distribution of yields after direct drilling) to show that the reliability of the technique had improved steadily with time and experience. Failures in earlier years were due to such factors as competition from grass weeds, especially couch grass, from slugs, 'ponding' of the surface soil, smeared slits, and failure of drills to penetrate on dry soils. In other words, in the earlier years we tended to bump into problems, not surprisingly, as we were all learner-drivers at that time! One very large area of ignorance concerned the suitability of soil types for direct drilling and reduced cultivation, and it was not until the mid and late 1970s that matters had advanced sufficiently to enable the classifications of soil suitability to be made. This is dealt with in detail in Chapter 4.

Davies and Cannell considered the evidence concerning nutrient requirements on direct drilled crops derived from the field experi-

Table 11. Relative yields of winter wheat and spring barley after different cultivation treatments in experiments started (a) before and (b) after 1970

Mean yield after ploughing = 100
(no. of experiment years in brackets)

Period and cultivation treatment	Winter wheat			Spring barley		
	After grass	After arable	All sites	After grass	After arable	All sites
Before 1970						
Direct drilling	91 (55)	90 (7)	91 (62)	87 (38)	97 (19)	90 (57)
Shallow cultivation	94 (30)	88 (5)	93 (35)	90 (26)	100 (16)	94 (42)
Deep cultivation	109 (2)	89 (7)	96 (9)	97 (1)	102 (17)	101 (18)
After 1970						
Direct drilling	100 (2)	98 (25)	98 (27)	— (0)	97 (29)	97 (29)
Shallow cultivation	— (0)	98 (46)	98 (46)	— (0)	99 (38)	99 (38)
Deep cultivation	— (0)	98 (25)	98 (25)	— (0)	100 (20)	100 (20)

NB. An experiment year means *one* experiment carried out for *one* year, therefore three experiment years could be one experiment or three years of three experiments each carried out for one year (author)

(Source: Davies & Cannell 1975) (Ref.4)

Table 12. Yield of direct drilled spring barley at one site 1970–4 (yield as percentage of ploughed plots)

Location	Soil type	Year					
		1970	1971	1972	1973	1974	Mean
Warminster, Wilts	Chalk loam (Ick-nield series)	101	104	105	90	103	101

(Source: Acknowledgement to ICI Agricultural and Plant Protection Divisions)

ments, and this is described in Chapter 3. They also underlined the need for an examination of the drainage requirements of direct drilled crops, especially on heavy land, where the benefit of timeliness of sowing by that technique is likely to be greatest.

In a brief reference to fodder crops, Davies and Cannell pointed out that most of the critical work on kale was done by ICI in the 1960s and that almost all the development work concerned with the direct drilling of fodder crops was achieved by large-scale observation trials and case studies carried out by ICI Plant Protection Division and by ADAS.

Allen[1] dealt mainly with the experiences of ICI in the earlier experimental and development work, and highlighted the problems requiring solution, in particular those concerned with direct drilling on heavy land in the autumn, direct drilling winter cereals into killed grass sward (frit fly problem) and direct drilling in the presence of straw. These aspects are all discussed in later chapters.

OTHER EXPERIMENTS

Although this chapter deals mainly with the agronomic objectives of the field experiments carried out and completed between 1961 and 1974 the following account of ADAS trials in East Anglia (1972–80) is included here because the main thrust of that work has been agronomic.

Many other experiments were started within the period covered by this chapter at the ARC Weed Research Organisation, ARC Letcombe Laboratory, Edinburgh School of Agriculture, SIAE Edinburgh, and Leeds University. As those experiments covered a rather wider field, and as many of them investigated fundamental aspects of soil/plant relationships, they are discussed in Chapter 3.

EXPERIENCE WITH WINTER CEREALS ON HEAVY EAST ANGLIAN SOILS 1972–80[11]

During the early years of direct drilling development the view was expressed frequently that whilst the benefits likely to be gained from direct drilling cereals should be greatest on the heavier soils, it seemed that such soils presented the greatest obstacles to the successful adoption of the system. The track record of direct drilling winter cereals on heavy land in those days was indeed far from impressive—smearing, compaction, ponding, and consequent poor stands of direct drilled cereals occurred more frequently than was comfortable! As knowledge deepened, experience broadened, and direct drilling machinery improved, however, the position changed completely.

A considerable contribution to this increased knowledge of direct drilling clay soils has been made by ADAS Eastern Region (Agronomy, Soil Science, Mechanisation and Plant Pathology Depts) which, in 1972, started a series of experiments initially on clay soils in East Anglia, but including some lighter land. The number of experiments has varied each year.

At the 1980 harvest there were:

two in their 8th year of winter wheat (heavy clay soils)
one in its 7th year of winter wheat (heavy clay soil)
one in its 6th year of direct drilling (winter barley in 1977–8)
four in their 5th year
two in their 3rd year
two in their 2nd year.

The number of years for which experiments have continued at any one site has varied—several have been conducted for one year only, and some have been concluded after 2–4 years.

Yield results of the whole project up to 1980 harvest are given in terms of 'best yields' below:

Number of sites where each treatment has given the best yields (Mean yields in t/ha in brackets)

Crop	Ploughed or deep cultivated	'Minimal cultivated'	Direct drilled
Winter wheat(1973–76)	9 (5·4)	10 (5·3)	13 (5·4)
(1977–80)	8 (6·4)	11 (6·6)	16 (6·7)
Winter barley	11 (5·7)	5 (5·6)	1 (5·4)
Spring cereals	7 (4·2)	5 (4·1)	1 (3·8)

The main inferences to be drawn from these summarised results are:

1. That on heavy soils direct drilling winter wheat produced best yields more frequently than either ploughing or reduced cultivation. In 1976 it was notable that at one site direct drilling

could be carried out satisfactorily when surface conditions on ploughed and cultivated land were unsuitable for sowing.

2. That on lighter land ploughing and minimal cultivation resulted in higher yields than direct drilling for all except two sites (one winter barley and one spring cereal). Some of these soils, classified as brown sands low in organic matter, can compact quite severely. Even winter barley, with a long season in which to compensate for early setbacks, did not establish too well on such soils when direct drilled (though there is some evidence that at higher rates of N it may do so), and spring cereals performed indifferently. Soils in north Norfolk just east of the Wash are typical of these compacting sands, which would be placed in Category 3 by the classification evolved by Cannell *et al.* (see Chapter 4).

3. In the wet autumn of 1974, coulter/soil interactions were studied, and it was noted that the triple disc coulter caused excessive smearing where the soil was compacted and wet at the time of drilling. Where this occurred germination of the seed was, at best, delayed, and frequently much reduced; furthermore, slug damage increased and the harmful effects of straw decomposition were more obvious. It was clear that under wetter soil conditions a tined coulter or a single disc would be preferable.

Naturally where plant populations were seriously depleted, yields on direct drilled plots were sometimes lower but, provided the *initial* populations were high enough, there was no evidence from the 1974 experiments that soil conditions in direct drilled plots affected subsequent yield except where drainage was inadequate. Work by Ellis and Barnes at Letcombe provided some explanation of this. They demonstrated that in a well-drained clay soil, though heavy rain and consequent 'ponding' caused a temporary decline in the root count in the 20–50 cm soil horizon on direct drilled land, once the water table was lowered (i.e. as spring progressed) root counts in that zone increased in direct drilled plots and were back on level terms with the ploughed plots (see Chapter 3 page 49).

4. Response to N was checked on the three treatments under test (ploughing, reduced cultivation and direct drilling) in all years of the series. Taking one year (1974) as an example, grain yields from direct drilling were lower than from ploughing in the absence of N. At 80 kg/ha N yields were similar on all three treatments, and at the highest level of N (157 kg/ha) direct drilling yielded best. Moreover, the yield on the ploughed plots had

'peaked' before that level, whereas the response to N on the reduced cultivation and direct drilled plots was still rising steeply.

The lower yield from direct drilling in the absence of N has been noted by various workers, and probably results from differences in the rate of mineralisation of N—this being possibly slower on the undisturbed soil.

REFERENCES

1. ALLEN, H. P. (1975), *Outl. Agric.*, **8** (Special No), 213–15.
2. ARNOTT, R. A. and CLEMENT, C. R. (1972) *Nature*, Lond. (4843), 29 Sept. 1962, 1227–8.
3. BULLEN, E. R. (1964), *Ann. Rep. Boxworth E. H. F. (MAFF), 1964*, 9–11.
4. DAVIES, D. B. and CANNELL, R. Q. (1975), *Outl. Agric.*, **8** (Special No.), 216–21.
5. HOOD, A. E. M., JAMESON, H. R. and COTTERELL, R. (1963), *Nature, Lond.* (4869), 23 Feb. 1963, 748.
6. HOOD, A. E. M., JAMESON, H. R. and COTTERELL, R. (1964), *Nature, Lond.* (4924), 14 March 1964, 1070–2.
7. HOOD, A. E. M., SHARP, D. G., HALL, D. W. and COTTERELL, R. (1964), *Proc. 7th BWCC, 1964*, 907–17.
8. JEATER, R. S. L. and LAURIE, D. R. (1966), *Weed Res.*, 1966, **6**, 332–7.
9. JEATER, R. S. L. and MCILVENNY, H. R. (1965), *Weed Res.*, 1965, **5**, 311–18.
10. JEATER, R. S. L. (1966), *Proc. 8th BWCC*, 1966, 874–83.
11. MAFF. ADAS. (1975, 1978, 1979, 1980), (i) *Expt. Dev. Rep. ADAS. E. Region*, 1975–80; (ii) *Results of Agric. Service ADAS Expt*, 1980, 27, Pt. I (In press).
12. WHYBREW, J. (1965), *Agriculture*, **72** (1965), 522–6.
13. WHYBREW, J. (1967), *NAAS Qtrly. Rev.*, **80** (1967), 154.
14. WHYBREW, J. (1969), *Agriculture*, **76** (1969), 497–501.

Chapter 3

THE EFFECTS OF ALTERNATIVE METHODS OF CULTIVATION ON SOIL CONDITIONS AND PLANT GROWTH

The early experiments and field development projects were conducted in the main on well-structured soils where continuous cereal cropping was a practical proposition. Most of the investigations focused on the energy- and labour-saving potential of direct drilling. They showed that on those 'easier' soils direct drilling could achieve cereal grain yields on a par with ploughing, provided that certain fairly simple guidelines were followed; in particular that preparatory work such as straw disposal and stubble weed control was carried out properly. Substantial savings of energy and labour were achieved and beneficial changes in soil structure were demonstrated.

Most of the traditional cereal-growing areas of the United Kingdom, however, are on heavier soils, clays and silts—soils which require large inputs of energy and labour for ploughing. Continuous cereal cropping on such soils can lead to some structural deterioration. Could direct drilling overcome or at least reduce this deterioration, and allow these heavier soils to be exploited more fully for long runs of cereals, especially winter cereals? This was the challenge for the 1970s.

The 1960s were the pioneering years and the 1970s the decade during which studies on soil–plant relationships produced significant advances in our knowledge concerning direct drilling. It will be helpful to consider these studies in chronological sequence.

Experiments at the Edinburgh School of Agriculture 1966–9[31, 50]
Spring barley is far and away the most important cereal grown in Scotland and the implications of direct drilling this crop on a sandy clay loam/loam soil (with clay loam/sandy clay loam subsoil) were

investigated in an experiment mounted by Holmes and Lockhart of the Edinburgh School of Agriculture from 1966 to 1969. Yields, growth and development of roots and shoots of the barley crop as well as response to applied nitrogen formed the main lines of investigation. Soane, Campbell and Herkes (SIAE Edinburgh) studied the effects of the contrasting cultivation methods for continuous barley growing on soil physical conditions.

Holmes and Lockhart discovered, as had others before them, that there was a close and positive correlation between N rate and cultivation system, in particular that at nil N or low N rates yields on direct drilled plots were inferior to those on ploughed and/or cultivated plots, but that these differences more or less disappeared as the rate of N was increased. They found also that, on average, root length was less on the direct drilled plots, though the roots were thicker, and they ascribed this difference to the physical state of the soil.

Soane and Campbell's soil studies demonstrated an inverse relationship between root length and dry soil bulk density; the higher bulk density, and therefore the shorter roots, being due to lack of tillage in the top horizon of the soil. This topic will be dealt with in more detail later.

ICI Experiment at Jealott's Hill 1968–9—Finney & Knight[27]

This experiment was in a way a watershed in that it signified a move away from straightforward field investigations to closer studies of the crop plant, in particular its roots, and it was conducted on a soil considered marginal for the establishment of a direct drilled crop. The field selected was a sandy loam (11·5% clay, 22·0% silt, 66·5% sand) with only moderate drainage properties.

From germination onwards the rate of elongation of the seminal root axes was slower following direct drilling; lateral branching also started earlier and was shallower than on the ploughed plots. Finney ascribed this shallower rooting system to the slower extension rate of the main root axes, which in turn could be correlated with pore size, the direct drilled soil being characterised by a smaller proportion of pores large enough to accommodate roots than was the case on the ploughed plots. Moreover, the direct drilled soil was clearly less easily deformed and more rigid than the ploughed soil.

In this particular experiment no significant differences between treatments were recorded in tiller production, dry weight, nutrient content or grain yield in spite of the observed differences in root development, and Finney points out that this was not unexpected as cereal crops produce more extensive root systems than are required for crop growth under average conditions. Nonetheless, the experiment pointed very clearly to the need for further investigations along similar lines, especially on more 'difficult' soils.

The Weed Research Organisation/Letcombe Laboratory Joint Tillage Project (1969–78)

Until the late 1960s the ARC, though interested in the general idea of alternative cultivations, had not engaged directly in any research work in this new field. The WRO, however, saw this as an important area for investigation and credit must be given to that Institute and in particular to Mr J. G. Elliott, for stimulating ARC involvement. The first major activity was a joint operation involving WRO and Letcombe.

Both of these research centres had basic interests in these new systems; the WRO because of the implications of chemically assisted direct drilling on weeds and weed incidence, and Letcombe because of their particular concern with soil–plant relationships and the influence of tillage systems on those relationships.

By the end of the 1960s there was adequate confirmation that direct drilling and reduced cultivations could give acceptable results on 'good' free-draining soils, free from perennial weed problems. Commercial development of direct drilling on such soils was beginning, albeit slowly. At the same time there had been failures, both in experiments and in farm practice, which could not be explained, partly because measurements and observations were not always sufficiently wide-ranging to provide explanations of the cause or causes of failure. For this reason, and in order to achieve a more complete understanding of the interaction of direct drilling and reduced cultivations with soil conditions, crop growth, and agronomic requirements, a series of experiments was started jointly by WRO and Letcombe. These compared the effects of direct drilling, tine cultivation and ploughing on the growth of winter and spring cereals, and on soil conditions over a number of years. Three contrasting soils were chosen:

1. Spring barley on a free-draining sandy loam overlying sandy clay soil at WRO Begbroke (a winter wheat experiment on this soil was started in 1972).
2. Spring barley and winter wheat on a calcareous clay at Buckland (Oxon).

3. Spring barley and winter wheat on a silty loam over chalk at Compton.

Table 13. Summary of cereal grain yields obtained after different cultivation treatments in the Letcombe Laboratory/Weed Research Organisation Joint Tillage Project 1969–78

Crop and soil type	Number of harvests	Average yield after ploughing t/ha	Yield as percentage of that after ploughing		
			Tine cultivated		Direct drilled
			Shallow	Deep	
Spring barley					
Isle Abbots series (sandy loam), Begbroke	5	5·02	99	97	97
Andover series (silt loam over chalk), Compton	4	3·70	107	105	104
Evesham series (clay), Buckland	4	4·76	101	100	100
Winter Wheat					
Sutton/Aldreth series (sandy loam), Begbroke	5	4·02	104	103	99
Andover series, Compton	4	5·77	98	96	99
Evesham series, Buckland	4	4·91	104	95	104

(Source: Ellis et al. (Letcombe); Elliott & Pollard (WRO), ARC Letcombe Ann Rep. 1978, p. 12)

Table 13 displays yield results achieved in these experiments.

It will be seen that, with the exception of the spring barley on the sandy loam at Begbroke, direct drilling produced yields more or less the equal of those from other cultivation treatments. Indeed, on spring barley at Compton and winter wheat at Buckland direct drilling yields were superior to those from ploughing.[17]

Ellis, Elliott and colleagues[23] examined the effects of the differing cultivation systems on soil physical conditions and root growth of spring barley at Begbroke. They found:

1. That greater soil compaction occurred in all the years of the experiment after direct drilling.
2. The growth of seminal roots of young cereal plants was reduced by direct drilling in each year (1969–73) but only in the first year were the differences significant.
3. Similarly, in each year, early shoot growth was reduced by direct drilling but, except for the first year, the barley plants compensated for this setback.

4. Direct drilling resulted in more earthworms being present in the soil.
5. The surface soil was more friable under direct drilling.
6. The surface soil on direct drilled plots also contained a higher concentration of available P and K.

Letcombe Longer-term Experiments (started 1974)

The joint experiments described above were on soils capable of sustaining long runs of cereals, either sandy loams or well-structured clays. While this joint series was still in progress Letcombe embarked upon a new series of experiments, this time with the objective of studying how soil conditions and crop growth are affected when different cultivation practices are employed for many years on soils liable to structural damage, or excessive wetness during the autumn and winter. The series started in 1974 and is scheduled to continue until 1984.

These experiments compare direct drilling, shallow tine cultivation and ploughing on three heavy, structurally 'difficult' soils: two clays, at Northfield, Oxon (Lawford series) and Compton Beauchamp, Oxon (Denchworth series), and a silt loam at Englefield, Berks. (Hamble series). (N.B. Shallow tillage was *not* included at Compton Beauchamp.) The crop rotation of winter wheat, winter oats, winter wheat and oilseed rape was followed in order to minimise interaction between cultivation treatments, and attack by pests and diseases.

AGRONOMIC RESULTS

At Englefield, spring wheat in 1974 and winter wheat in 1976 yielded significantly less from direct drilling than from ploughing, but in 1977 direct drilling gave better yields than ploughing at all three sites. On the clay soil at Buckland, direct drilling consistently produced higher yields of winter wheat, but at Compton Beauchamp yields from direct drilling in 1975, 1978 and 1979 were only moderate.

Averaged over the first four years of these long-term experiments (1974–8), however, similar yields resulted from each of the cultivation treatments, but the *ratio* of the yield following direct drilling to that following ploughing has varied more from year to year at Englefield and Compton Beauchamp than at Northfield. At Northfield direct drilling, produced a significantly heavier yield over the period (on average 6 per cent higher) than did ploughing.[7]

It is of interest to compare the results on the silty loam at Englefield with those obtained in a four-year experiment carried out on similar soil in eastern Scotland between 1970 and 1974. Grain yields of direct drilled cereals (both winter wheat and spring barley) were markedly lower than from conventional cultivation, even at high levels of nitrogen (113 kg/ha–128 kg/ha) with higher bulk density and lower porosity at the 5–10 cm depth on direct drilled plots.[51]

ROOT DISTRIBUTION

It might be expected that undisturbed soils would be more compact, with lower total porosity and a greater resistance to root penetration, than ploughed or cultivated soils, and, indeed, various experiments have confirmed this. For example, the experience with spring barley on the sandy loam at Begbroke in the WRO/Letcombe Joint Tillage Project (see page 45) was that bulk density was highest on the direct drilled plots in each of the first three years of the experiment.[23] Likewise, Douglas, Goss and Hill[14] found that soil bulk density was lower and total pore volume (also volumes of the larger 'transmission' pores) was greater on ploughed and cultivated plots on the clay soil at Compton Beauchamp (see Table 14). The *continuity* of these larger pores was clearly greater on the direct drilled plots than after ploughing, however, because these pores were not destroyed by cultivation. This confirmed earlier observations at Jealott's Hill.[52]

Table 14. Bulk density profile to 40 cm after direct drilling and after ploughing to 25 cm depth on a clay soil (Denchworth series) 1977

Depth (cm)	Bulk density (g/cm³)		Significance level of difference
	Direct drilled	Ploughed	
0–5	0·91	0·82	*
5–10	1·00	0·91	*
10–15	1·03	0·94	**
15–20	1·12	0·95	*
20–25	1·19	1·08	*
25–30	1·26	1·22	NS
30–35	1·30	1·29	NS
35–40	1·34	1·35	NS

*significant at P = 0·05
** significant at P = 0·01 (highly significant)

(Source: Douglas, Goss & Hill, Letcombe) (Ref. 14)

This work and other experiments have shown that, to quote Ellis and Barnes, the 'restraint imposed on root growth by mechanical stress must not be assessed purely from measurement of these *bulk* properties of a soil. In the field roots grow down the faces of the soil blocks (peds) and through pores, including the continuous cylindrical channels produced by the movement of earthworms—in other words the purely structural properties of a soil may not be a completely reliable indication of the ability of plant roots to ramify through that soil; the existence of a continuous system of pores or channels of sufficient diameter to accommodate roots is a more important factor.'[20]

It has already been mentioned that the Begbroke experiment on spring barley[23] and the root development studies at Jealott's Hill[27] found that in the early stages of plant development the axes of the seminal roots extended more slowly on undisturbed or shallow (5 cm) cultivated soils than on ploughed or cultivated soils disturbed to a depth to 20 cm; furthermore, that on the former soils lateral branching of the roots occurred earlier. At Begbroke, however, when the same treatments were reapplied to the same plots in successive seasons, differences between treatments lessened, which suggested that conditions had become more favourable for root growth. Bakermans & de Wit[1] had found earlier that though there were fewer roots in the 10–30 cm horizon on direct drilled than on cultivated soil, lower down the root density was at least as great on direct drilled as on ploughed or deeply cultivated land. These experiments (at Begbroke and in Holland) were on coarse-textured soils.

Ellis and Barnes[20] extended their studies first to the calcareous clay site at Buckland (1972–5) and then to the heavier clay soils at Northfield and Compton Beauchamp (1975–8). The method used for evaluating root distribution is described in their paper. As they found no consistent differences in root development between direct drilled and shallow tine cultivation treatments, or between ploughing and deep tined cultivation, comparisons were restricted to direct drilling and ploughing. Main points arising from this series of experiments were:

1. With winter-sown cereals, and *during the early stages of plant establishment* the root systems of plants recovered by digging did not usually show any significant difference between direct drilling and ploughing either in numbers of seminal roots or in density of lateral development (contrast this with the results on spring barley at Begbroke[23] and Jealott's Hill[27]).

2. Winter measurement of roots at various depths in the sandy

loam and on the calcareous clay (at Buckland) in the years 1971–5 show progressive increases in depth of penetration throughout the winter in both soils irrespective of cultivation treatments. During this period *average* rate of penetration *per day* was 5 mm.

3. On the calcareous clay at Buckland in 1975, from the beginning of February until the end of March, there was extensive 'ponding' and the water content of the surface 5 cm of soil in the direct drilled plot was consistently higher than on ploughed soil. Between 5 cm and 20 cm the water content was lower on the direct drilled plots. Root measurements were made at three dates: 11 February, 22 February and 8 April. Between the first and second dates there was a decline in the root count between 20 cm and 50 cm depth on the direct drilled areas and a small increase in the root count on the ploughed soil. During March and early April, however, there was rapid root growth on the direct drilled soil in response to a lowering of the water content of that soil, which largely compensated for the earlier decline. During this period there was no change in the density of roots on the ploughed plots.

Other workers[6] have noted that in wet conditions larger concentrations of N_2O have been measured in direct drilled clay soils than in ploughed soils, indicating the presence of anaerobic zones within the soil peds; this may explain the decline in root numbers mentioned above.

An interesting point to note is that although this differential growth pattern with different cultivation systems occurred in the 20–50 cm horizon, downward penetration of roots in the 50–80 cm zone continued on both direct drilled and ploughed soil at similar rates. The situation at the beginning of stem elongation of winter wheat in the experiment on calcareous clay at Buckland (averaged over 3 years) is illustrated in Table 15.

The *sum* of counts at this stage was consistently greater on direct drilled than on ploughed land.

4. In the spring of 1976 Ellis & Barnes followed up their work at Buckland with investigations on the non-calcareous clays at Northfield (Lawford series) and Compton Beauchamp (Denchworth series). Both soils had cracked extensively in 1975. At Northfield, in each of the years 1976, 1977 and 1978 consistently more roots were counted through the soil profile after direct drilling than following ploughing. Several of the differences were statistically significant (between 40 cm and 100 cm depth in 1977 and at 20, 30, and 50 cm depth in 1978). Results at Compton Beauchamp were similar in 1975–6 but in 1977–8 there was higher than average winter rainfall; as a result, roots penetrated less deeply, *and where root*

Table 15. Root count profiles for winter wheat on direct drilled and ploughed calcareous clay soil (Evesham series) at stem elongation (3-year average 1973–5)

Soil depth cm	Root counts per m² Direct drilled	Ploughed
20	1010	850
30	810	650
40	610	490
50	440	370
60	340	270
70	130	160
80	20	10
TOTAL	3360	2800

(Source: Ellis & Barnes, Letcome 1980) (Ref. 20)

samples were taken at a time when no appreciable loss of water from the soil had been recorded, more numerous roots were found on the ploughed plots. It was noted, however, that, as the water content of the direct drilled soil was lowered, rapid root growth followed.

Drew & Saker[16] reported experiments at Buckland and Compton Beauchamp, mounted in the unusually dry season of 1975–6. The objectives were to investigate the distribution of extractable phosphorus and potassium, and of roots, in the top soil in the second year of the direct drilling experiment on these two sites. The nutrient study will be considered later but the major indications concerning root distribution were that:

● Direct drilling usually led to greater compaction at the surface soil, not necessarily detrimental.
● Direct drilling of spring barley at Buckland (calcareous clay) led to greater rooting density at the end of tillering in the upper 5 cm of soil in 1976 (as it had in 1975), and there was a similar response from winter wheat at Compton Beauchamp (non-calcareous clay).

It is important to note that in the Letcombe experiments root growth on the clay soils after direct drilling was impaired only after soil waterlogging in the winter. Once the water content of the top soil was lowered, root growth on the direct drilled plots was rapid; indeed, when the soil had dried appreciably in the period before sampling, a greater quantity of roots was found on the direct drilled soil than on the ploughed land, and this was very marked and persistent in 1976.

These experiments indicate that on direct drilled soils the roots of the drilled crop, ramifying through cracks and through channels left by old roots and by earthworms, are better able to reach and exploit sources of water in the soil at depths greater than 1 metre; this correlates well with heavier grain yields obtained on the direct drilled plots under drought conditions. In these undisturbed soils the water content below 50 cm was greater than on ploughed soils,[28] so direct drilling in a dry year offered the twin advantages of deeper root penetration and a larger reservoir of water which these deeper roots could tap. Measurements made in 1976 showed that the wheat crop was able to extract 22 mm more water from the direct drilled soil than from the ploughed soil.

Investigations by Hodgson and others at Leeds University between 1971 and 1974[30] on spring barley on a clay/sandy clay loam of the Wothersome series confirmed some of the Letcombe findings. In the Leeds work five cultivation systems for spring-sown barley were tested over this four-year period. Four of the cultivation systems involved primary cultivations in the autumn (shallow—7·5 cm, medium—15 cm, deep—23 cm tine cultivations) and mouldboard ploughing (23 cm deep). These were compared with spring direct drilling following weed control with aminotriazole and paraquat (post emergence weed control was with mecoprop or mecoprop/2,4D). Treatments were repeated on the same plots each year. Straw was burnt on all plots prior to autumn cultivations. Although there were infestations of volunteer barley each autumn on the direct drilled and shallow cultivated plots, neither weeds nor diseases interfered with the experiments.

Mean yields over the four years did not differ significantly, though direct drilling and shallow tine cultivation yielded significantly less than deep tine cultivation and ploughing in the second year of the experiment. The estimated net energy required for direct drilling was only one-eighth of that needed for ploughing.

As with the Letcombe studies, soil strength and bulk density were greater with direct drilling but this had only a small effect on root distribution throughout the profile, i.e. in direct drilled plots the proportion of the root system was less in the 2·5–12·5 cm layer and greater in the 12·5–32·5 cm layer than in any of the cultivation treatments.

THE MOVEMENT AND RETENTION OF SOIL WATER

The Letcombe experiments provided an opportunity for the study of distribution and movement of water in heavy soils. Results from the calcareous clay at Buckland and from the two non-calcareous clay soils at Northfield and Compton Beauchamp were similar, so a consideration of the Compton Beauchamp results gives an indication of the general response to all three soil types. Observations made at the time of maximum water content in the contrasting winters 1974–5 (wetter than average) and 1975–6 (much drier than average) show that after the winter of 1974–5 (rainfall 350 mm) the water content of the ploughed soil was greater than that of the direct drilled soil at the 20–100 cm layer; in contrast, in the spring of 1976 and after a winter rainfall of only 160 mm the water content was generally greater in the direct drilled than in the ploughed soil, especially in the 50–100 cm horizon.[28]

Sometimes, however, especially in fine-textured and unstable soils, infiltration of rain water may be considerably slower through the surface soil. Thus after heavy rain its water content when undisturbed may be higher, and that of the lower soil horizon considerably lower than after ploughing (see Table 16).[26]

Table 16. Water content of surface layers of a clay soil after a period of high rainfall

Soil depth	Water (g per 100 g dry soil)	
cm	Direct drilled	Ploughed
0—5	70·0	60·1
5—10	51·4	61·5
10—15	49·2	58·1

(Source: Ellis, Letcombe 1975) (Ref. 26)

In the summer of 1976 bare soil plots on a clay soil, some ploughed and some direct drilled, were irrigated with known quantities of water applied as a spray and avoiding 'run-off'.[28] Thirty minutes after irrigation with 15 mm of water, while very little had penetrated below cultivation depths of ploughed land (20 cm), it had reached a depth of 70 cm on direct drilled land. Furthermore, when this treatment (15 mm water) was repeated for six successive days, though the water content increased in both soils to a depth of 100 cm the soil of the ploughed plots contained more water, especially in the region of the plough 'sole' (25 cm depth). These results show:

● that water from a 'shower' of rain, penetrated more rapidly in direct drilled land;
● that with repeated applications of water, ploughed land became wetter than the undisturbed land, certainly below 10 cm depth.

This rapid movement of water down the profile of direct drilled clay soils seems to be due, as with root penetration, to the greater continuity and numbers of cracks, root channels and earthworm burrows in undisturbed soil.

Further tests in the dry spring/summer of 1976 showed that from mid-March to the end of tillering in mid-April more water was extracted from the 20–50 cm layer of ploughed soil than from the same layer of direct drilled soil. Taking the whole 60–100 cm layer, by mid-June (flowering) significantly more water had been extracted from the direct drilled soil. It will be recalled that in the early spring of 1976 roots were more numerous at depth from the direct drilled plots; as there was also more water at depth in the undisturbed soil, it is a further indication that the greater withdrawal of water from the deeper soil layers in that dry season contributed to the higher yields achieved by direct drilling on the clay soils under tests.

Two Dutch workers[54] had already noted that different cultivation treatments can have a marked influence on structure and porosity of upper soil horizons such that the water potential of superficial layers after wetting may remain higher for longer periods with direct drilling than with ploughing. They suggest that this may arise from water retention by organic residue and decayed roots, and from the capillary transport of water. The latter is probably greater in the more compact structure in the surface of direct drilled soil compared with the loose, rough surface of ploughed land.

One fact not hitherto mentioned concerns the effect of straw-burning. This matter will be considered more fully later but it is interesting to note (see table 17) that results of investigations by Ellis, Douglas & Christian[22] suggest that burning of straw or stubble residues may increase infiltration of rain water or evaporation from the soil surface or both.

Note that, two weeks after straw burning (after rain had fallen) the soil water had increased appreciably over the whole area, but significantly less on the burnt plots.

THE STABILITY OF SOIL AGGREGATES

The stability of aggregates (i.e. groupings of soil particles), determines the nature of the soil structure. The presence of clay particles confers stability (or strength) on these soil aggregates, so it is important to know what effect different cultivations may have on this stability. At Letcombe Douglas[13] concluded that direct drilling, by leaving a higher level of organic matter in the surface layers of soil,

Table 17. Effect of burning the straw from a previous crop on the water content in the surface layer (0–5 cm) of a clay soil (Denchworth series—Compton Beauchamp)

	Time after burning (weeks)	Straw burnt	Straw not burnt	Least sig. diff. (P = 0·05)
Soil water content	0	7·0	7·0	—
(g/100 g soil)	2	32·5	44·4	4·5
	9	48·1	55·4	2·7
Total porosity (percentage of total soil volume)	9	67·5	68·8	1·8
Water saturation* (per cent)	9	61·3	66·6	4·5

*Volume of water-filled pores as percentage of total pore volume
(Rainfall after burning 2 weeks—27·5 mm
                          9 weeks—188·5 mm)

(Source: Ellis et al., Letcombe 1976) (Ref 22)

can lead to greater stability of the soil aggregates. The results of Douglas's experiments are shown in Table 18.

Table 18. Effect of cultivation on the stability and organic matter content of soil in the surface 2·5 cm of a calcareous clay (Evesham series) at Buckland, Oxon

Treatment in previous four years	Stability measurement (T) for aggregates 1·4—2·8 mm	Organic matter content
Direct drilled	0·560	5·83
Shallow-tine cultivated	0·574	5·83
Deep-tine cultivated	0·555	5·43
Ploughed	0·527	5·05
Least sig. diff (P = 0·05)	0·039	

(Source: J T Douglas, Letcombe, 1976) (Ref. 13)

The constant T used as a measure of stability is not important in itself. What is important is that the higher the value of T the greater the aggregate stability; from this it can be seen that direct drilling and shallow tine cultivation confer greater stability on the soil in question than do deep tine cultivation or ploughing. Furthermore, there is a close correlation between aggregate stability and the level of organic matter in the surface layer of soil, and indeed roots themselves, by producing exudates of organic substances and mucigel, together with root residues, can contribute directly to the stability of soil aggregates. Table 19 shows the results of investigations at Jealott's Hill.[52]

Table 19. Stability of soil aggregates in a sandy loam after two years of ploughing or direct drilling

Depth	per cent of high stability aggregates	
(cm)	Ploughed	Direct drilled
0 – 2·5	7	36
2·5 – 5·0	2	6
5·0 – 10·0	10	17
10·0 – 15·0	20	11

(Source: after Tomlinson, Jealott's Hill, 1974) (Ref. 52)

There are numerous recorded instances of the surface tilth increasing after a number of years of direct drilling (see plates 1 and 2). It must be noted, however, that wet conditions can cause slaking and disrupt the soil aggregates. Thus even if at the end of summer the surface tilth on direct drilled land may be appreciable, a wet winter following may cause deterioration, especially on heavy land. Plates 3, 4 and 5 illustrate the situation on an Oxford clay. Photograph 3 shows a good friable tilth immediately after direct drilling winter wheat, and plates 4 and 5 show a comparison of the soil surface on another part of the same field before and after spring cereals were drilled in the following year after a wet winter. The deterioration of the tilth due to the high rate of rainfall on this soil is obvious.[46]

Douglas[13] also studied the soils of the long-term tillage experiments, particularly the non-calcareous clay soils at Northfield and Compton Beauchamp. He found that the condition of the surface tilth at drilling time was better in those areas where the straw was completely burnt than on other areas where the straw was either chopped or left as stubble (see also Ellis, Douglas and Christian[22]).

OXYGEN CONCENTRATION IN THE SOIL

It would be assumed that the movement of oxygen in the soil would be affected differentially in line with the changes in the porosity of the soil following direct drilling (compared with ploughing). Numerous workers have expressed the view that more restricted aeration would be expected in uncultivated soil than in ploughed soil, because of the higher bulk density and fewer large pores. On

PLATE 1
First year of direct drilling on a sandy loam soil.   Outlook on Agriculture (1975)

the other hand it has been demonstrated[4] that aeration may be *promoted* in undisturbed soil because the continuous channels formed by cracking, old roots and earthworms have not been destroyed by deep cultivation.

Boyce & McCalla[5] found that reducing cultivations on moderately light soils had relatively little effect on oxygen levels, and the only work on the topic so far recorded on heavier land is that of R. J. Dowdell and colleagues.[15] These workers carried out a study of oxygen concentrations following direct drilling and ploughing systems on the calcareous clay soil at Buckland, a soil of low hydraulic conductivity, during the three years 1973–5. This soil consists of 40 per cent clay and 2·2 per cent organic carbon in the 15 cm layer. During each of these three seasons the land was sown with winter wheat. Results were:

1. In the relatively dry winter of 1972–3 mean concentrations of oxygen—expressed as volume of oxygen as a percentage of the volume of soil (v/v)— were:
   15 cm depth . . . 20% v/v
   60 cm depth . . . 12% v/v.
2. In the wetter winters of 1973–4 and 1974–5 mean oxygen concentrations were:

PLATE 2
Same field as in Plate 1. taken just before the *fifth* successive spring barley
crop was direct drilled.   Outlook on Agriculture (1975)

PLATE 3
Surface soil on Oxford clay *immediately* after direct drilling.
                                            Outlook on Agriculture (1975)

PLATE 4
Another part of the same field as in Plate 3 before direct drilling barley in the following spring; the deterioration of the tilth is due to wet conditions in winter.   Outlook on Agriculture (1975)

PLATE 5
Same field *after* direct drilling the barley.   Outlook on Agriculture (1975)

15 cm depth ... less than 11% v/v
60 cm depth ... less than 6% v/v.

3. Direct drilling resulted in higher concentrations of oxygen at 15 cm depth than ploughing in both winters:

    direct drilling ... 10·3% v/v ⎫ (means of two winters—see
    ploughing ... 7·2% v/v   ⎬   Table 20).

    Furthermore, when the oxygen concentration at 15 cm decreased to its annual minimum in the January/March period, a significantly higher number of sampling points under direct drilled soil continued to register oxygen concentrations greater than 10% v/v.

4. The only occasions when direct drilling resulted in significantly *lower* concentrations of oxygen than ploughing at 15 cm depth occurred during a four-week period in the late autumn of 1973 when there was an unusually low rainfall before ploughing. The workers concluded that a more open structure of the soil created by ploughing and cultivation would have permitted freer gas exchange between the air and the soil until the heavy winter rain caused the cultivated layer to slump.

Table 20. Effects of cultivation on mean concentrations of oxygen – averaged results for the three months January–March in two winters, 1973–4 & 1974–5

Depth (cm)	Oxygen concentration per cent (V/V)		Least sig. diff. (P = 0·05)
	Direct drilled	Ploughed	
15	10·3	7·2	2·4
30	8·4	5·7	n.s
60	3·9	5·3	n.s

(Source: Dowdell et al., Letcombe, 1979) (Ref. 15)

Dowdell and his colleagues point out that the major routes by which oxygen and water enter soils of low hydraulic conductivity are the planes of weakness between soil blocks (peds), holes created by earthworms, and channels left after roots have decayed. Indeed, they refer to the earthworm population data derived from the Letcombe experiments (see Table 21) as supporting evidence for the existence of a better system of continuous channels in uncultivated soil. This would explain both the higher concentrations of oxygen in direct drilled soil at 15 cm depth, and the less frequent occurrence of low oxygen concentrations at 15 cm and 30 cm depths in wetter winters, than on ploughed soil. They conclude by saying that further work is required to estimate how respiration rate is affected by different cultivation methods and warn that, before any general conclusions can be drawn, more information concerning oxygen concentration under different cultivation systems is needed from other soils, particularly those of higher water and clay content.

Table 21. Earthworm population in a clay soil (Evesham series) at Buckland, which had been direct drilled or ploughed in successive years 1973–6

Crop and year of experiment	Date of sampling	Number of earthworms		Ratio $\frac{D/D}{P}$
		Direct drilled	Ploughed	
Spring barley				
Year 1	1st Oct 1973	145	110	1·3
2	1st Oct 1974	345	218	1·6
3	20th Oct 1975	231	98	2·4
4	20th Nov 1976	197	50	3·9
Winter wheat				
Year 4	26th Nov 1976	152	95	1·6

(Source: Ellis & Barnes, Letcombe, 1977) (Ref 19)

(When looking at Table 21 the reader should note that differences with winter wheat may be smaller because there is less damage when cultivation is completed within a few weeks than when autumn ploughing is followed by secondary cultivation in the spring.)

NUTRIENT UPTAKE

For the sake of clarity this aspect is considered separately from others, but obviously the uptake of nutrients depends on factors influencing root distribution, oxygen concentration and water movement; what has been said about these aspects must be borne in mind when discussing nutrients.

Nitrogen

As is well known, nitrogen is taken up by the plant roots as nitrate and the optimum availability of this major element depends on soil conditions being such as to encourage conversion of optimal quantities of applied nitrogenous fertiliser (or nitrogen derived from organic residues) into the nitrate form.

Nitrogen, as nitrate, is able to move *to* plant roots by diffusing in continuous films of water in the soil, also by bulk diffusion as water moves through the soil; thus nitrate availability is not greatly affected by soil structure. On the other hand, potassium, ammonia, sodium, magnesium and calcium, as cations, move less by either of these diffusion processes because they are held as positive ions in response to negative charges on the surface of soil colloids; thus to absorb these elements roots must move to *them*. For this reason uptake of these particular nutrients is considerably affected by soil structure. Phosphorus (of which more later) is relatively immobile and depends on roots moving to a source of phosphorus supply; again therefore phosphorus is sensitive to changes in soil structure, thus sensitive to cultivation systems which affect that structure.

The factor most likely to affect nitrogen availability is waterlogging which leads to anaerobic conditions and loss by denitrification. Thus plough pans and compact layers, by holding up water in the top soil, will reduce nitrate supply to roots.[10]

It has been noted that direct drilled cereal crops, in the early stages of establishment, display visual symptoms indicative of limited nitrogen supply (a paler green leaf). Quite often also it has been apparent that in the first year of direct drilling of a particular soil the nitrogen required for a direct drilled crop is higher than that required for a conventionally cultivated crop.[12,1,31] This is often ascribed to the slower mineralisation of nitrogen in the uncultivated soil. On the heavy clay soil at Compton Beauchamp it was noted in one year that the relatively low oxygen concentration in the surface layer led to denitrification. On this particular soil, however, it is of interest to record that, though the nitrogen in the shoots of winter wheat, measured at the end of tillering, was lower after direct drilling than after conventional sowing, differences at flowering time were very small. In contrast to this, Hodgson and his colleagues at Leeds found that over a two-year period mean nitrogen uptake by spring barley was least in direct drilled crops; they attributed this to the slower rate of mineralisation of soil nitrogen in untilled plots.[30]

To generalise, a trend has been observed in many field experiments in which direct drilling and ploughing have been compared. Conventionally established crops, in particular cereals but also kale, have been seen to perform better at low levels of nitrogen; however, direct drilled crops continue to respond to nitrogen after yields on conventionally sown crops have 'peaked'. This was exemplified in ADAS experiments in East Anglia in 1974 and 1975.[43] In that same trial series in 1976–7 it was noted also that early (i.e.

March) N top dressing on winter wheat produced more tillers on direct drilled and shallow tine-cultivated plots but the proportion of those tillers bearing ears was lower than in the ploughed plots.[44] At Buckland in 1976–7, however, the response of wheat to a range of levels of nitrogen (from 0–200 kg/N/ha) was not affected by the cultivation system employed (direct drilled for five years; direct drilled for one year; or traditional cultivation). The only difference (and this was highly significant statistically) was in favour of April application compared with May application.[21]

The same general trend was apparent at the other two clay soil sites at Northfield and Compton Beauchamp, but in 1978 there *was* an interaction between N and cultivation treatments at those two sites. These contrasting results are not surprising, as 1977 (no response) was a relatively dry year, and 1978 (response) was wet.

Davies & Cannell[12] in describing direct drilling experiments carried out between 1957 and 1974 attempted a survey of the information yielded by these experiments on the question of nitrogen requirement. They pointed out that:

● the correct way to compare yields resulting from the contrasting cultivation systems is to choose yields from *optimum* levels of N for each treatment. Comparison of direct drilling with ploughing at similar N levels for each system resulted in serious underestimates of yields from direct drilling.

● Most of the wheat experiments for which the direct drilled nitrogen requirement exceeded that of the ploughed treatment were on clay soils, supporting the view that direct drilled crops grown on soils with slower natural drainage, where conditions tend to favour denitrification, are more likely to need additional nitrogen fertiliser.

Davies & Cannell drew up a table which is reproduced here (see Table 22) summarising, from the rather limited direct drilling experiments reported between 1970 and 1974, mean nitrogen requirements for winter wheat and spring barley as indicated by those experiments. They underlined limitations to the value of the figures, firstly because levels of fertiliser N applied were not high enough to reach optimal levels for both direct drilling and ploughing and/or secondly the increments in fertiliser nitrogen used in the trials were too large. Nonetheless, the table has some indicative value.

PHOSPHORUS AND POTASSIUM

Work in the United States in the 1960s[47,53] had shown that after six

Table 22. Mean nitrogen fertiliser requirements (kg N/ha) for highest yield of cereal after direct drilling or ploughing

Crop and nature of experiment	Requirement (kg N/ha) After direct drilling	After ploughing	(no. of experiment years)
Winter wheat			
All experiments	95	85	(45)
Where lower after ploughing	120	54	(10)
Where higher after ploughing	51	104	(4)
Where requirement same for both	92	92	(31)
Experiments where optimum established for each treatment	74	63	(15)
All since 1970	137[a]	124	(5)
Spring barley			
All experiments	107	86	(39)
Where lower after ploughing	120	69	(16)
Where requirements same for both	98	98	(23)
Experiments where optimum established for each treatment	81	58	(14)
All since 1970	88[b]	88	(7)

[a] Mean yield 7% greater than after ploughing
[b] Mean yield 1% greater than after ploughing

(Source: Davies & Cannell 1975.) (Ref. 12)

years of contrasting cultivation ranging from zero tillage (i.e. direct drilling) to full conventional systems (mouldboard plough plus secondary cultivations) the concentrations of extractable P and K in the upper soil horizons were greater with zero tillage than with deep cultivation; in the latter treatment P & K were uniformly distributed throughout the soil layer.

In spite of this surface accumulation of extractable nutrients in undisturbed soil, there was no evidence from this United States work to show that crops suffered during drought periods because of desiccation of surface soil and the superficial roots therein. Indeed, the concentrations of P and K in the shoots in direct drilled crops were at least as high as in plants grown on deep cultivated soils. The earlier work[49] in particular, demonstrated that direct drilled maize absorbed surface-applied P as well as when P had been deeply incorporated by cultivation, or placed at seed depth. The surface mulch from killed grass sod and/or previous crop residues may possibly have maintained a sufficiently moist environment to encourage root growth and exploitation in the surface layer of soil, thereby ensuring adequate uptake of nutrients.[53]

United Kingdom work has also shown that P and K accumulate in the surface layers of soil where crops have been direct drilled[45,30,24] and experiments by Drew & Saker[16] on two of the soils studied in the Letcombe experiments (Compton Beauchamp and Buckland) have produced similar results. Another suggestion was made in addition to this fairly obvious conclusion (i.e. that if soil is not inverted surface-applied nutrients tend to concentrate in the surface soil). This was that the release of P and K from straw burning and from decomposition, and mineralisation of plant residues either *on* the surface or, in the case of decayed roots, *in* the surface layer of soil, would also contribute to the accumulation of these nutrients. Drew & Saker indicated, however, that this trend towards the development of concentration gradients P and K may be offset by:

1. An acceleration of the release of these nutrients from fertiliser residues or mineral reserves deeper in the soil, as a response to the depletion of the more mobile forms of P and K by roots.
2. The movement of top soil, rich in P and K, down cracks and fissures which develop as soils (especially clay soils) shrink.
3. P, *in solution* being taken to considerable depths by water moving through large pores and channels after heavy rain.

Cannell and Graham[8] put this matter of nutrient uptake into perspective. They found that though it might be expected that in a very dry season such as 1975–6 direct drilled crops would suffer because they would not be able to absorb the P and K concentrated in the dry surface soil, this was not the case. Differences in concentration of P and K in the shoots of winter wheat grown under contrasting cultivation treatments were small, which suggests that 'the amounts of nutrients absorbed may have been governed mainly by the ability of the plants to utilise the nutrients for growth and that the supply available to roots under both treatments (i.e. direct drilling and ploughing) was adequate despite the contrasting distribution of nutrients in the soil'[8] (see Table 23). Cannell & Graham add that on soils of lower nutrient status, however, there may be different results. Later work confirmed these findings.

THE EFFECT OF STRAW RESIDUES

Until comparatively recently, cereal straw was not considered to

Table 23. Content of nitrogen, phosphorus and potassium in the shoots of winter wheat at different stages of growth, and in the grain at harvest, after direct drilling or ploughing on a clay soil (Denchworth series, 1975–6). (Results expressed as weights of N.P & K.)

Growth stage (Feekes–Large scale)	Nutrient	Concentration mg/g dry weight		Total content (kg/ha)	
		Direct drilled	Ploughed	Direct drilled	Ploughed
End of tillering	N	38·5[b]	40·9	65[b]	86
(GS.5)	P	4·41	4·40	7·5[b]	9·3
	K	41·0	44·8	70[b]	95
Flag leaf emerged	N	17·0[b]	18·6	121	136
(GS.9)	P	2·72	2·71	19·5	20·0
	K	30·9	31·7	221	233
Flowering	N	11·6	12·0	142	140
(GS.10·5)	P	2·28	2·17	27·7	25·4
	K	19·6	20·0	238	235
Harvest	N	10·9[b]	12·1	136	140
(Total shoots)	P	2·27	2·18	27·2[b]	24·2
	K	10·2	10·6	167	173
	N	18·2[b]	19·9	103	101
Grain	P	4·05	3·82	22·9	19·4
	K	4·65	4·22	26·3	21·5

[b] significantly different from ploughed (P = 0·05)
(Source: Cannell & Graham, Letcombe, 1976) (Ref. 8)

cause any particular problem. It was utilised in the farming cycle, its fate depending on the presence or absence of livestock on the farm, also on the price at which it might be sold to other farmers. On farms with livestock, straw was used for feed and bedding, and much of it was eventually returned to the land in the form of farmyard manure. On arable farms without a livestock enterprise the straw would be sold off the farm or ploughed in.

Nowadays, very many large arable farms growing cereals on an intensive system have no livestock enterprise, and baling, carting and selling the straw is often an uneconomic proposition. The straw must therefore be disposed of and, as there is much to do in the autumn, and only a short interval between harvesting one lot of cereals and planting the next, more and more farmers are burning their straw, irrespective of which cultivation system they employ.

The view is held by some that this is wasteful, and that an opportunity to return valuable organic matter to the soil is being thrown away. Careless burning, leading to inconvenience and on occasion to serious accident, lends strength to those who oppose straw burning, and of course it is beyond argument that slipshod methods of burning straw are at best antisocial and, at worst, downright dangerous. The technical argument in favour of ploughing in straw as a means of preserving valuable organic matter is weak, however, as has been demonstrated on many occasions, for example in straw disposal trials on ADAS experimental husbandry farms,[48] also by work at Sprowston,[29] High Mowthorpe,[42] and Rothamsted.[11] Results from the latter work demonstrated that returning straw to land over long periods increased the organic carbon content of the ploughed layer by a mere 0·2 per cent. Having said this, it must be conceded that there may be advantage in the annual incorporation of straw in soils of poor structural properties of low organic matter content.[34] It has also been shown that where straw (or other organic material) with a relatively high ratio of carbon to nitrogen (C.N) is added to the soil, the micro-organisms decomposing the straw utilise the nitrogen which is then immobilised and rendered unavailable to the subsequent crop until the C.N ratio is lowered. It was calculated many years ago that 8 kg of nitrogen per tonne of straw was thus utilised, so that when the 7·5 tonnes of straw per hectare (a reasonable yield for a good crop) is ploughed in and decomposes, about 60 kg per hectare of nitrogen is immobilised.[33]

Since the advent and development of direct drilling and reduced cultivations systems, attention has necessarily been focused on straw residues and associated problems. In the very early experiments conducted by ICI, NAAS and others (see Chapter 2) difficulties were encountered when cereal seeds and straw were pushed into drilled slits in close proximity, with resulting very mediocre stands of cereal seedlings. Some of the reasons for this poor establishment of cereal crops were obvious. In some cases the seeds never made contact with the soil; they chitted in the straw and, when a dry period followed emergence, they died. In other instances it was noted that straw residues harboured slugs which then attacked the newly drilled seeds and seedlings along the slits.

Disposal of cereal straw is thus essential for successful direct drilling, and until and unless a useful, profitable outlet is established for the by-product (such as an energy source or for paper making), it appears that the present most economic way of removing straw is by burning. The porportions of straw baled, chopped and burned in England and Wales in 1977 are displayed in Table 24.[32]

Investigations have been carried out at Letcombe Laboratory on

Table 24. The fate of straw in the field in England and Wales—Mean results for 1976 and 1977

| | *per cent of total area* | | |
Crop	Baled	Chopped and spread	Burnt
Wheat	42	6	52
Barley	82	1	17

(Source: after Hughes 1979) (Ref. 32)

the effect of straw residues on cereals, especially on direct drilled crops, and these are reviewed here. The visual effects of straw residues on direct drilled crops are observable in the early stages of crop establishment—lower plant populations arising out of poor germination or seedling death. Some other symptoms resemble nitrogen deficiency (for example, reduced tillering, short, spindly plants), yet they have not been corrected by additional N. Immobilisation of N has already been mentioned, but it has been postulated following the Letcombe experiments that adverse effects of straw (and weed) residues on direct drilled cereal crops may arise:

1. through the production of phytotoxins of crop residues decaying under wet conditions, either leached out of the straw or produced by microbial activity;
2. through fungal colonisation, likely to be greater
   a) in the surface layers of undisturbed soil, and
   b) in the presence of crop residues on the surface.[39,41,3,2,38,25]

Production of Phytotoxins

Laboratory studies on decomposing straw taken from direct drilled slots in the field, showed that six days after barley seeds were grown in the suspension of this straw (in distilled water) growth (particularly shoot growth) was adversely affected compared with 'control' plants[18] (see Table 25).

Lynch's work in 1976–8[35,36,37] indicated that under aerobic conditions (i.e. with adequate oxygen), straw decomposed rapidly and there was little accumulation of soluble carbon products. Under anaerobic conditions a considerable amount of these products formed, mainly as organic acids of which the major component was acetic acid (others being proprionic and butyric in small amounts). Acetic acid was evolved in a concentration sufficient to inhibit root growth of a wide range of species (including wheat, clover and

Table 25. Effect of decaying straw on the development of barley seedlings. Mean result for ten plants

	Control	Straw residue present
Number of seminal roots per plant	5·8	6·0
Total length of seminal roots (mm per plant)	76·9	11·6
Total dry weight, excluding seed coat (g per plant)	0·115	0·062
Ratio $\dfrac{\text{root dry weight}}{\text{shoot dry weight}}$	1·16	0·72

(Source: Ellis et al., Letcombe, 1974) (Ref. 18)

oilseed rape). Lynch also found that this inhibiting concentration of acetic acid exists only in the immediate vicinity of the straw, and 1·5 cm away from the straw the concentration is reduced by 50 per cent. The important stage of decomposition when this evolution of acetic acid would be most marked is about two to three weeks after direct drilling and concurrent incorporation of straw in direct drilled slits, and this appears to coincide with the time at which these phytotoxic effects become most evident.

Decaying rhizomes of couch grass (*Agropyron repens*) also produce acetic acid in phytotoxic concentration. Lynch showed, however, that in experiments on this grass death of barley seedlings in soil plots containing dead rhizomes of couch grass was greater in relatively dry soil. Had this death of seedlings been due only to the production of acetic acid by rhizomes, one would have expected the effects to be greater in the wetter soil—clearly another factor was involved and this is considered below.

Affects of Direct Drilling on Microbial Activity of Soil in the Presence of Straw Residues

Experiments at Letcombe[3] indicated that under direct drilling a more varied microflora is developed which is concentrated in the surface soil, especially the pathogens *Fusarium*, *Cephalosporium* and *Phoma*. The incorporation of straw residues into direct drilled slits will stimulate greater development of these pathogens, to the detriment of the direct drilled seedlings. Referring again to the work on couch grass mentioned above, Lynch concluded that the death of barley seedlings on drier soil was probably due fo the synergistic effect of acetic acid *and* one such pathogen, e.g. *Fus-*

arium culmoreum.

Certain saprophytic fungi, capable of living on dead matter, in particular *Mucor hiemalis* and *Gliocladium roseum*, tend to colonise seeds under anaerobic conditions and obstruct the entry of oxygen into the seed—these organisms are also more numerous on surface layers of undisturbed soil and where crop residues are present.

Other Effects of Straw Residues

The treatment of straw residues before drilling has been shown to influence the earthworm population. In general terms the populations of earthworms between 1971 and 1976 on the soil used in the Letcombe experiments were consistently larger on direct drilled than on the ploughed land, and this applied to deep burrowing and surface-inhabiting species alike. These population differences were greater with spring-sown crops than with autumn-sown crops. Their response to different straw treatments depended on species, however; significantly larger numbers of deep-burrowing species were found on the chopped and spread area, whereas where straw was burnt the number of the surface living *Allolobophora chlorotica* were significantly greater.

Table 26 demonstrates the effectiveness of straw burning in increasing yields of winter wheat. This is very evident with direct drilling but obvious even after ploughing, and is derived from the results of three years of experiments at five EHFs.[9]

Table 26. Yields of winter wheat following different straw disposal methods 1974–6. (Three-year averages as percentage of yield on burnt areas)

	Straw treatment		
Cultivation	Burnt	Baled	Chopped
Ploughed	100	91	91
Cultivated	100	87	89
Direct drilled	100	78	78
Mean	100	85	86

(Source: After Collins, *Big Farm Management*, July 1977) (Ref. 9)

To summarise, it seems clear that the general experimental evidence is against the view that the addition of straw to most soils improves conditions and leads to increased yields. Incompletely decomposed straw can offer mechanical hindrance to drilling, especially with direct drilling and minimal tillage methods. Moreover the presence of straw in close proximity with drilled seeds under anaerobic conditions is likely to lead to poor seedling development. These ill effects are likely to occur in just those situations where the benefits which may accrue from direct drilling are potentially greatest. This leads to the conclusion that, in the present state of the art, the disposal of straw by burning is a necessary preliminary to successful direct drilling or minimal tillage—burning, that is, with due regard to the NFU Code of Practice for Straw Burning.

It should be added that chemical methods of alleviating some of the ill effects of straw residues have been investigated at Letcombe with some success; for example, dusting seed with chalk to increase the pH around the seed to counteract the acetic acid, and seed treatment with fungicides to combat the effect of pathogenic fungi.[25,40]

REFERENCES

1. BAKERMANS, W. A. P. and DE WIT, C. T. (1970), *Neth. J. Agric. Sci.*, **18,** 225–46.
2. BARBER, D. A. and HAYNES, JANICE C. (1977), *Rep. A.R.C. Letcombe*, 1976, 61–3.
3. BARBER, D. A. and STANDELL, CHRISTINE (1977), *Rep. A.R.C. Letcombe*, 1976, 58–60.
4. BARNES, B. T. and ELLIS, F. B. (1979), *J. Soil Sci.*, **30,** 669–79.
5. BOYCE, J. S. and McCALLA, T. M. (1969), *Soil Sci.*, **105,** 241–8.
6. BURFORD, J. R., DOWDELL, R. D. and CREES, Rachel (1977), *Rep. ARC Letcombe*, 1976, 71–2.
7. CANNELL, R. Q., ELLIS, F. B., CHRISTIAN, D. G., GRAHAM, J. P., JACKSON, R. and WAKELEY, TORFRIDA (1979), *Rep. A.R.C. Letcombe*, 1978, 13–14.
8. CANNELL, R. Q. and GRAHAM, J. P. (1977), *Rep. A.R.C. Letcombe*, 1976, 40–1.
9. COLLINS, A. (1977), *Big Fm. Mgmt.*, July 1977, 21–4.
10. COOKE, G. W. (1962), *2nd B.W.C.C. Symposium*, 1962.
11. COOKE, G. W. (1967), *Control of Soil Fertility* (Crosby, Lockwood & Son Ltd), 202 & 439–53.
12. DAVIES, D. B. and CANNELL, R. Q. (1975), *Outl. Agric.*, **8** (Special No.), 216–20.
13. DOUGLAS, J. (1977), *Rep. A.R.C. Letcombe*, 1976, 40–8.
14. DOUGLAS, J. T., GOSS, H. J. and HILL, D., *Soil & Tillage Res.*, **1** (1980/81), 11–18.
15. DOWDELL, R. J., CREES, RACHEL, BURFORD, J. R. and CANNELL, R. Q. (1979), *J. Soil Sci.*, **30,** 238–45.
16. DREW, M. C. and SAKER, L. R. (1980), *J. Agric. Sci. Camb.*, **94,** 411–23.

17. ELLIOTT, J. G., ELLIS, F. B. and POLLARD, F. (1977), *J. Agric. Sci. Camb.*, **89**, 621–9.
18. ELLIS, F. B., BARBER, D. A. and GRAHAM, J. P. (1975), *Rep. A.R.C. Letcombe*, 1974, 39–40.
19. ELLIS, F. B. and BARNES, B. T. (1977), *Rep. A.R.C. Letcombe*, 1976, 50.
20. ELLIS, F. B. and BARNES, B. T. (1981), *Plant & Soil*, **55**, 283–95.
21. ELLIS, F. B., CHRISTIAN, D. C. and GRAHAM, J. P. (1977), *Rep. A.R.C. Letcombe*, 1976, 45–6.
22. ELLIS, F. B., DOUGLAS, J. T. and CHRISTIAN, D. G. (1977), *Rep. A.R.C. Letcombe*, 1976, 49–50.
23. ELLIS, F. B., ELLIOTT, J. G., BARNES, B. T. and HOWSE, K. R. (1977), *J. Agric. Sci.*, **89**, 631–42.
24. ELLIS, F. B. and HOWSE, R. K. (1980), *Soil Tillage Res.*, I (1980/81), 35–40.
25. ELLIS, F. B. and LYNCH, J. M. (1979), *8th Conf. Inst. Soil Till. Res.*, 1979, Istro Bundesrepublik Deutschland.
26. ELLIS, F. B. (1975), Personal Communication.
27. FINNEY, J. R. and KNIGHT, J. A. G. (1973), *J. Agric. Sci. Camb.*, **80**, 435–42.
28. GOSS, M. J., HOWSE, K. R. and HARRIS, W. (1978), *J. Soil Sci.*, **29**, 4, 475–88.
29. HARVEY, P. N. (1959), *J. RASE,* **120**, 55–63.
30. HODGSON, D. R., PROUD, J. R. and BROWNE, S. (1977), *J. Agric. Sci. Camb.*, **88**, 631–44.
31. HOLMES, J. C. and LOCKHART, D. A. S. (1970), *Proc. Int. Conf. Till. Res. Methods Silsoe*, 46–57.
32. HUGHES, R. G. (1979), *Straw Decay and its Effect on Utilisation and Disposal*, J. Wiley & Son Ltd., Chichester.
33. HUTCHINSON, H. B. and RICHARDS, E. M. (1921), *J. Min. Agric.*, **28**, 398–411.
34. JOHNSTON, A. E. (1979), *MAFF ADAS Rep. 4th Straw Utiliz. Conf.*, Oxford.
35. LYNCH, J. M. (1976), *C.R.C. Critical Rev. Microbiol*, **5**, 67–107.
36. LYNCH, J. M. (1977), *J. Appl. Bact.*, **42**, 81–7.
37. LYNCH, J. M. (1978), *Soil Biol. Biochem.*, **10**, 131–5.
38. LYNCH, J. M. and GUNN, K. B. (1977), *Rep. A.R.C. Letcombe*, 1976, 56–8.
39. LYNCH, J. M. and HARPER, S. H. T. (1977), *Rep. A.R.C. Letcombe*, 1976, 54–6.
40. LYNCH, J. M. and HARPER, S. H. T. (1978), *Rep. A.R.C. Letcombe*, 1977, 50–2.
41. LYNCH, J. M., HARPER, S. H. T. and PRYN, S. J. (1977), *Rep. A.R.C. Letcombe*, 1976, 60–1.
42. MAFF, ADAS (1964), *High Mowthorpe E.H.F. 4th Ann. Rep.*
43. MAFF, ADAS, Eastern Region (1975), *Expt. Dev.*, 1975, 93–6.
44. MAFF, ADAS, Eastern Region (1978), *Expt. Dev.*, 1978, 31–43.

45. RILEY, D., COUTTS, J. and GOWMAN, M. A. (1975), *Proc. No-Tillage Forage Symp.* (Ohio State Univ.), 15–28.
46. RUSSELL, R. S., CANNELL, R. Q. and GOSS, M. J. (1975), *Outl. Agric*, **8** (Special No.), 227–32.
47. SHEAR, G. M. and MOSCHLER, W. W. (1969), *Agronomy Journ.*, **61**, 524–6.
48. SHORT, J. L. (1973), *Exptl. Husbandry*, **25**, 103–6.
49. SINGH, T. A., THOMAS, G. W., MOSCHLER, W. W. and MARTENS, D. C. (1966), *Agronomy Journ.*, **58**, 147–8.
50. SOANE, B. D., CAMPBELL, D. J. and HERKES, S. M. (1970), *Proc. Int. Conf. Till Res Methods*, Silsoe, 58–76.
51. SOANE, B. D. and RODGERS, J. B. A. (1974), *Exptl. Husbandry*, **27**, 68–71.
52. TOMLINSON, T. E., *Trans. 10th Int. Congr. Soil Sci*, **1**, 203–11.
53. TRIPLETT, G. B. and VAN DOREN, D. M. (1969), *Agronomy Journ.*, **61**, 637–9.
54. VAN OUWERKERKE and BOONE, F. R. (1970), *Neth. J. Agri. Sci.*, **18**, 247–61.

Chapter 4

THE SOIL AND DIRECT DRILLING

For the information and advice given in this chapter I am deeply indebted to the ADAS Soil Scientists, Dr D. B. Davies and Mr B. Wilkinson; to Dr R. Q. Cannell and his colleagues of Letcombe Laboratory, ARC, and to Dr D. Riley and Messrs M. Gowman and J. Coutts of ICI Plant Protection Division.

Dr Davies has dealt with this topic in detail, and his views and counsel are published in *Soil Management*[2] and *Cereals without Ploughing.*[7] Dr Cannell, in conjunction with Dr Davies and others, has categorised United Kingdom soils according to their suitability for direct drilling,[1] and the ICI workers in a joint unpublished report,[5] also Gowman[6] have described the results of their studies on 150 direct drilled fields, visited and inspected in 1973–5. As the reports of all these workers tend to overlap to some extent, this chapter is divided into two parts, the first dealing with the categorisation of soils according to their suitability for direct drilling (covering the work of Wilkinson, and of Cannell and others), with some mention of their bases for classification. The second part describes the results of the ICI survey work, in particular the advice given to enable farmers to determine in which of the 'suitability categories' their soils might be placed, together with some guidance concerning identifying and overcoming soil problems which can affect direct drilling.

SUITABILITY OF UNITED KINGDOM SOILS FOR DIRECT DRILLING—CLASSIFICATION

Wilkinson[10] and Cannell and colleagues[1] classified the soil types occurring in cereal growing areas of Britain according to their suitability for direct drilling. Both Wilkinson and Cannell used published experimental results from direct drilling experiments conducted between 1961 and 1974 as the basis for their classifications, and both described soil and other factors leading to, or likely to militate against, the successful use of the technique. Both workers cover much the same ground, whilst expressing their conclusions in different ways. Wilkinson classifies soils on the basis of probability of success of direct drilling, and lists for each of his three probability categories (high, moderate and low) the soil/site definitions covering the category. He gives examples of soil groups and soil series for each category. Cannell and his colleagues list factors favourable and unfavourable for successful direct drilling; they display a map of the major cereal growing areas, divided into the three categories of soil suitability, and they classify the soils in the National Soil Survey Map according to the same categories. As the Cannell work was later than that of Wilkinson, and therefore able to draw upon evidence published up to and including 1977, the major points arising from that survey are reproduced here. Note that the classification of soil suitability refers to direct drilling of *combine-harvested* crops.

BASIS FOR CLASSIFICATION

Sources of information
Cannell and his co-workers drew their experimental evidence from crops sown mainly with triple-disc drills, occasionally with tine drills, usually followed by light cultivations with harrows to cover the seed.

The suitability of the soil for direct drilling was considered in terms of the likelihood of loss of yield from growing crops without cultivation in comparison with traditional methods based on the mouldboard plough or heavy tined implements. It was assumed that such traditional cultivation would be optimal, i.e. conducted with adequate labour and machinery under optimal conditions. The experiments used as the 'source material' naturally had limitations—in many experiments only one level of nitrogen had been used and few of them took into account the capability of more timely sowing which could be conferred by direct drilling. The results of experiments where poor management was identified as the major cause of loss of yield *either* with direct drilling *or* with ploughing were excluded from consideration.

Limiting soil factors
Forces acting upon soil fall into two categories, i.e. those which tend to compact, and those which tend to loosen. The former are referred to below; the latter include frost action, the effects of

alternate wetting and drying on clay soils, and cultivations aimed at relieving compaction. Soils suitable for direct drilling need to possess inherent properties which favour non-limiting soil bulk density when in the normal (i.e. equilibrium) state. Some (but not all) less favoured soils may be *made* suitable for direct drilling by management practices designed to discourage compaction—such practices are referred to later in this chapter and elsewhere in the book.

Many of the soil factors limiting the chances of successful direct drilling have already been mentioned, but they merit repetition here as they form an important part of the basis for classifying soils. They include:

1. Lack of tilth—on soils liable to slake or slump after rain. Direct drilling may lead to inadequate covering of the seed, smearing of the drill slot if the soil is wet and 'ponding'—conditions which will in turn lead to greater loss from slugs.

2. Top soil compaction—wheels are the main source, though in weakly structured soils slaking after rain can also cause compaction. On excessively compacted soils direct drilling is obviously more at risk, from ponding and water erosion (via the slits) on wet soils, and from accentuation of drought effects in dry periods. Under conventional sowing systems timely cultivations can correct excess compaction. Resistance to compaction is associated with the following points—some are contributory to compaction and others help to correct it.

● *Drainage*
  Rapid draining soils are less at risk of compaction from wheeling and slaking because the strength of such soils is greater at lower moisture levels.

● *Texture*
  Loamy and peaty soils and some calcareous clays are relatively resistant to compaction. Sands, on the other hand, with low organic matter levels and with mixed particle size or a predominance of fine sand, tend to compact readily as do silts, sandy clay loams, and loamy sands containing clay-sized particles.

● *Organic matter*
  Additional organic matter reduces the effect of compacting factors—in this respect direct drilling over a number of years can itself reduce liability to compaction by increasing the content of organic matter in the surface soil.

● *Surface mulching*
  Calcareous clays and peats possess the property of self-

mulching, i.e. the capability of producing a good surface tilth, both summer and winter, by weathering.

● *Free lime*
Calcium carbonate in large quantities, naturally occurring and intimately mixed with the soil, confers great resistance to compaction compared with neutral or acid soils.

● *Wetness caused by slow subsoil drainage*
Where drainage is inadequate direct drilled crops are more susceptible than those conventionally drilled, possibly because the top soil under direct drilling contains less air-filled pore spaces, saturates more quickly, and the excess water is unable to drain laterally at 'plough' depth. 'Ponding' in subsoils is therefore more likely in direct drilling systems. Good field drainage will help but if the soil is slow draining, waterlogging may still be a risk.

● *Stones*
Very stony soils may offer problems of seed placement for direct drills but stones can also be a problem to the plough!

● *Slopes*
Cannell and Davies suggest that these represent some risk of gully erosion after drilling. On the other hand it has been demonstrated on a wide scale on the Appalachian slopes in Virginia and Kentucky that *only* by direct drilling can a crop be established without serious risk of erosion (see Chapter 12). With an irregular slope, admittedly, it may be difficult to direct drill to an even depth.

● *Springs*
Land liable to spring lines or liable to 'collect' water in wet periods is likely to be risky for direct drilling.

Climatic factors
Experience has certainly shown that in wet years, where there is an early return of the soil to field capacity in the autumn, and where the rainfall is high during seedling establishment, the success of direct drilling is at risk. But good management, careful planning before drilling, and sowing at the earliest date, will all help to make the technique more likely to work satisfactorily.

In wet summers and autumns there is a tendency for a vicious spiral to operate. Harvest is late, giving less opportunity for proper disposal of crop residues (burning straw and stubble is more difficult), also less time and opportunity for optimal weed control measures. There is a greater risk of 'ponding' and waterlogging, especially on less stable and weaker structured soil. Grass weeds, especially rough-stalked meadow grass, creeping bent and blackgrass, thrive in wet autumns, and finally there is more delay in spring drilling because of the surface wetness of uncultivated stubbles.

In taking account of all these constraints, Cannell and his colleagues have used date of return of soil to field capacity as an important index in their classification.

Major Cereal Growing Areas (see Fig. 1)
The soils classified are in those areas of Britain where more than 20 per cent of the agricultural land is used for growing cereals. Fig. 1 illustrates these areas and various categories are displayed.

PROVISIONAL SOIL CLASSIFICATION
The distribution of the three categories of soil to be described below is shown in Fig. 2.

Category 1 (see colour plate 6)
Soils with favourable properties on which yields similar to those from well-managed conventional cultivations can be expected from both autumn- and spring-sown crops. For instance: chalk and limestone soils; well-drained loamy soils; humous soils, peaty soils and peat. These frequently have substantial natural (free) lime in subsoil and topsoil, generally with high organic matter content (more than 2% in sands, 3% in loams and silts, and 5% in clay soils). Examples are: Cotswold brash soils, magnesian limestones, chalk downs, chalky boulder clay, Lower Lias clay, well-drained, well-structured loams, and brown soils.[2]

The sites should be level and not subject to spring lines or frequent surface flooding. Date of return to field capacity is not a limiting factor on these soils. This group covers about 30% of the cereal growing area of Britain.

Table 27. Category 1 soil groups

1	Rendzinas and brown calcareous earths (chalk and limestone soils)
2	Loamy brown earths and argillic brown earths (well and moderately drained soils)
3	Humic sandy gley soils (humic sands)
4	Humic alluvial gley soils (humic loams and clays)
5	Peat soils (organic soils)
6	Brown sands, brown calcareous sands and brown podzolic soils (coarse sands) with high organic matter

(Source: After Cannell, Davies, Mackney & Pidgeon *Outl. Agric.*, *9*, 6.1978, 313) (Ref. 1)

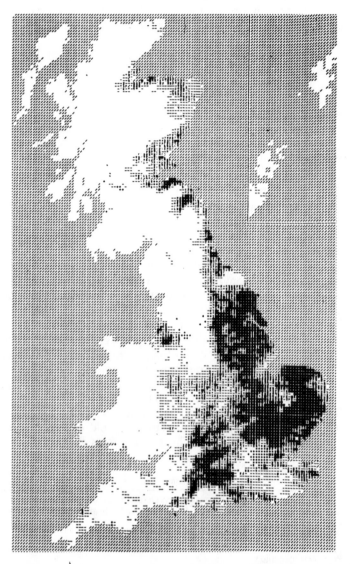

Fig. 1. Distribution of cereal-growing areas in Britain. Unshaded—less than 20 per cent of agricultural land growing cereals. Increasing shading = (a) 20–35 per cent, (b) 35–50 per cent, (c) over 50 per cent.   After Cannell et al., Outlook on Agriculture (1975)

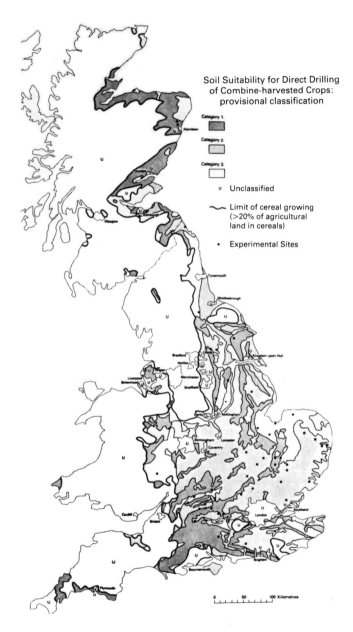

Fig. 2. Soil suitability for direct drilling of combine-harvested crops: provisional classification.

After Cannell et al., Outlook on Agriculture (1975)

Category 2 (see colour plate 7)

Soils where, with good management, the yield of winter cereals is likely to be similar after direct drilling and conventional cultivation but where the yield of spring-sown crops is likely to be appreciably reduced. This category includes calcareous clay soils, clayey or loamy and clay soils, imperfectly and moderately well-drained soils with some natural impediment to drainage which can be remedied to some extent by field drainage systems. This category also includes brick earth and silts.[2] Category 2 soils cover about 50 per cent of the growing areas but exclude areas where the return to field capacity of the soil is *before* 1st November.

Table 28. Category 2 soil groups

1 Argillic pelosols (non-calcareous clays)
2 Calcareous pelosols (calcareous clays)
3 Stagnogley soils* (clayey, loamy and loam over clay soils)
4 Loamy stagnogleyic, gleyic argillic and paleo-argillic brown earths
5 Stagnogleyic brown sands (with *high* organic matter content)
6 Cambic gley soils (loamy soils)

* Stagnogleys with unstable A horizons might belong more appropriately in Category 3 but at present evidence on such soils is lacking

(Source: After Cannell, Davies, Mackney & Pidgeon, *Outl. Agric., 9*, 6.1978 314) (Ref. 1)

Category 3 (see colour plate 8)

Soils in which there is a substantial risk of loss of yield after direct drilling, especially of spring sown crops;

● Wet, alluvial and clayey soils, especially (though not exclusively) where the mean date of return to field capacity is before 1st November. This category would include poorly drained, weakly structured clays, for example London Clay in Essex, Herts and Bucks.[2]
● Sandy and silty soils with low organic matter.
● Excessively well-drained soils and soils affected by fluctuating ground water and/or flooding.

Sites of *any* soil type subject to spring lines or to influx of water from higher areas or in any way subject to flooding, steeply sloping land with sharp variations in gradient, land with very stony patches, and fields with variable soil types which include some Category 3 soils, should all be considered as Category 3 even if the soil, as such, may be found under the Category 2 definition.

Table 29. Category 3 soil groups

Brown sands containing less than 2% organic matter	Sandy soils with low organic matter content, and silty soils
Silty argillic and paleo-argillic brown earths	
Certain other brown earths	
Podzols	
Gley-podzols	

Silty argillic gley soils

Alluvial gley soils, brown calcareous and brown alluvial soils (silty soils and soils subject to flooding)

Sandy gley soils (sandy soils)

Brown podzolic soils

Gley soils (poorly drained soils)

Stagnogley soils (poorly drained soils) and calcareous pelosols where the return to field capacity is before 1 November

(Source: Cannell, Davies, Mackney & Pidgeon, *Outl. Agric.*, *9*.6.1978 J.4) (Ref. 1)

Cannell and colleagues conclude from their work that 'an appreciable part of the cereal growing area of Britain would appear to be suited to sequential direct drilling at least for winter crops.' They warn that the classification made was drawn up using such information as was available at the time and that it may have to be extended and/or modified as knowledge increases and more experience is gained.

SOIL STRUCTURE

A field soil consists of aggregates of individual soil particles, e.g. sand, silt, clay, lime and organic matter. It is these elements which confer stability upon a soil. Aggregates themselves can differ in size, shape and mass, and the way in which these different types occur and are distributed throughout the top soil and subsoil determine the nature of the soil structure. Aggregates may be small granules or large blocks and plates. Fig. 3 shows a number of typical aggregates of arable soils.

In a well-structured soil the friable crumbs and granular aggregates predominate throughout the top soil, with blocks and prisms in the subsoil separated by wide vertical pores or fissures (see Fig. 4).

Granular and crumb

Found in topsoils
when well weathered
and cultivated.
Frost tilths of heavy soils.

Angular blocky

Fit together tightly in
profiles of heavy soils

Sub-angular blocky

More rounded and porous
than the 'blocky' aggregate
— in loams and other
well structured soils.

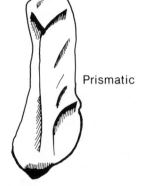

Prismatic

Subsoils of heavy soils

Platy

Plough pans,
compacted layers,
under slipping tractor
wheels.

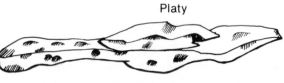

Fig. 3. Typical aggregates found in arable soils.   Davies, Eagle & Finney, 'Soil Management' Farming Press p. 81

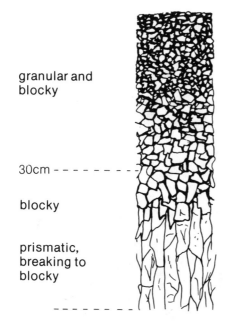

An open porous structure ideal for direct drilling.

granular and blocky

30cm - - - - - - - -

blocky

prismatic, breaking to blocky

- - - - - - - -

Fig. 4. A well-structured soil.   Davies, Eagle & Finney, 'Soil Management', Farming Press p. 88

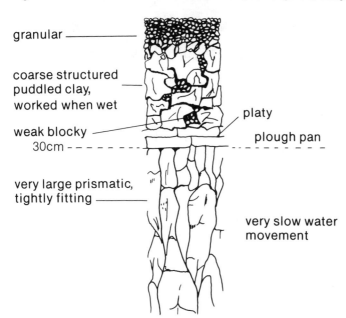

granular ————————

coarse structured puddled clay, worked when wet —

weak blocky ————

30cm - - - - - - - - -

platy

plough pan - - - - - - -

very large prismatic, tightly fitting ————

very slow water movement

Fig. 5. A clay loam with damaged structure.   Davies, Eagle & Finney, 'Soil Management', Farming Press, p. 89

PLATE 9
A silty clay loam with over-compact structure.

ICI Plant Protection Division

Fig. 5 and plate No. 9 show the typical distribution of soil aggregates in a clay loam which has been subjected to frequent cultivation down to plough depth. The soil at the surface consists of well-structured granular aggregates. However, below the top 10 cm the clay particles have been puddled, the aggregates are bigger, more compact and smeared, through cultivation of the soil when too wet. The plough pan consists of plate-like aggregates, and the subsoil, typical of many clays, consists of tight prism-like aggregates. Vertical communication through this soil is poor and root penetration through smeared aggregates and the plough pan is very limited.

Finally, there are the structureless sands and silts which are very unstable, very prone to slaking and slumping and have very few

PLATE 10
A weakly structured sandy soil.   ICI Plant Protection Division

pores. These soils contain too little of the stabilising elements: clay, organic matter and lime (see Fig. 6 and Plate 10).

ASSESSING SOIL AND IDENTIFYING PROBLEMS[1,2,5,6]

Soil Drainage Status
The main indicators of the drainage status of a soil are:
1. Top soil porosity
2. Subsoil porosity
3. Subsoil texture
4. Soil colour
5. Condition of plant roots.

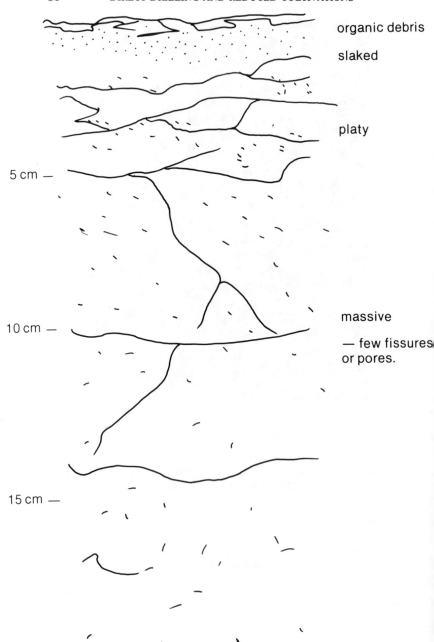

organic debris

slaked

platy

5 cm —

massive

— few fissures or pores.

10 cm —

15 cm —

Fig. 6. Sandy or silty soil with unstable structure.   M.A. Gowman, ICI Plant Protection Division

1 & 2. Porosity (top soil and subsoil)
A sufficiency of large pores, and freedom from compaction, giving good communication from top soil to subsoil, provides an adequate drainage system.

3. Texture of subsoil
The 'feel' of a soil to the touch will be a guide to its drainage status. If the soil is moistened and worked in the hand it will form a cohesive ball which is difficult to deform and, when moist, feels sticky (clay), smooth, soapy or buttery (silts), or gritty (sands). These are, of course, only very general guides. However, if the subsoils seem clayey they are likely to have low infiltration rates and water from the topsoil may find difficulty in getting away unless special provision is made for this through an adequate tile-drainage system with permeable back-fill supplemented possibly with moles.

4. Soil colour
Well-drained soils tend to be uniformly coloured—red, brown, yellow, throughout the top 100 cm.

Moderately drained soil would be similar down to 50 cm but may have a subsoil which lies wet for long periods and is 'gleyed'. Evidence of this will be 'mottling': grey/blue/green mottling in the case of permanently waterlogged subsoil whereas an interspersion of red or brown with the grey suggests a fluctuating subsoil water table. Poorly drained soil will be mottled up to within 30 cm of the soil surface, and the top soil will be dull in colour.

5. Condition of plant roots
Healthy roots are white with obvious root hairs—with waterlogging roots may become discoloured and may have brown tips.

By judicious use of a spade and auger the structure, porosity, and drainage status of top soil and subsoil may be assessed, but care must be taken to bring the spit-full of soil on to the surface with the minimum of disturbance. The soil can be studied layer by layer.

In the surface (0–5 cm) good features are:
● Friable aggregates which break down easily into crumbs when the edge of the spade is dragged through the surface.
● Signs of earthworm casts or burrows, indicating that there is adequate organic matter and good drainage.

Bad features are indicated by:
● Hard surfaces with few pores.
● Smearing when spade edge dragged through surface, leaving open slot (too wet or too heavy)
● Surface cap of slaked soil 0.5 to 5 cm thick, typical of an unstable, weakly structured soil.

● Ruts and puddles or 'ponding' indicate poor drainage.

In the top soil (5–25 cm) good features are:
● A range of aggregates of different sizes (see Fig. 4), firm to the touch but able to be crumbled by hand.
● Porous aggregates with roots growing through them.
● Vertical cracking.
● Earthworm channels.

Bad features are:
● Dense profile with few pores.
● Aggregates with roots growing round instead of through.
● Platy structure—horizontal cracking.

Soil Surface Conditions
Surface Compaction is a result of traffic and/or treading when the soil is too wet; soil crumbs tend to cement together. Provided the soil beneath the surface is porous and the seed is sown into this porous layer, germination and establishment may not be adversely affected, so long as weather at and after drilling remains reasonably dry. In wetter weather this surface compaction will lead to 'ponding'.

If there is a plough pan and/or inadequate subsoil drainage, this surface compaction problem will be made worse (see plates 11 and 12, which illustrate some effects resulting from drilling into compacted soils).

Smearing of the drill slot is likely to occur if a disc-type direct drill is used when the surface is wet and plastic. The slots remain open and the seed is exposed to weather and to birds. The degree of smearing is important; slight smearing may still allow roots to penetrate downwards provided conditions following drilling are not too dry (when the compressed soil may be hard and resistant) or too wet (with excess water still in the slot). Severe smearing, however, gives little scope for root penetration or drainage.

Slaking. Direct drilled soils with a certain amount of organic matter may be less susceptible to slaking which is a feature of unstable weakly structured soils with a low organic matter content.

Excessive Trash (see Chapter 3). This harbours slugs and reduces the effectiveness of the herbicide applied to the stubble weeds, fouls and blocks up drills, and leaches toxic chemicals which damage the drilled seed.

Variable Surface Soil Strength Causing Variable Drilling Depths
If drills are set up on relatively compacted headlands on sandy

PLATE 11
Lateral rather than vertical growth of kale roots. ICI Plant Protection Division

PLATE 12
Restricted root growth
in direct drilled
maize.
ICI Plant Protection Division

soils, the seed in mid-field may be drilled too deep. On heavy soils, drilling too deep, below the porous layer, is also likely to lead to reduced germination.

Structure of Subsoil

This can only be examined properly by excavating a pit and removing spades full of earth at subsoil depth at the side of the pit and assessing porosity, fissuring, packing of the soil blocks, etc.[2]

IDEAL SOILS

The following three photographs illustrate a medium soil, a light soil and a heavy soil, porous, open and well-structured and very suitable for direct drilling.

Plate 13 shows a calcareous loam typical of 'brash' soils, e.g. in the Cotswolds very suitable for direct drilling because:

- they are free-draining, overlying limestone bedrock;
- they are well-structured;
- they are self-mulching, i.e. they can maintain their structure;
- they are resistant to compaction, partly through their stone content;
- they have a reasonable earthworm population.

Plate 14 illustrates a well-structured sandy loam, a 'skirt' soil on the edge of the Fens. 'Skirts' vary in texture from heavy silty clay to light sandy soils, usually with a high organic matter content. Structure consists of friable crumbs with an adequate system of large pores.

Plate 15 shows a heavy soil with a silty clay texture, very difficult to work by traditional cultivation on an all-arable system. An adequate artificial drainage system of tile drains plus permeable back-fill is essential on such soils, supplemented by periodic moling to facilitate the movement of excessive water to the tile drains. The crumb layer is shallow (1–3 cm) with larger and more closely packed aggregates below this level, but these soil types are extremely porous and often have a high population of earthworms.

Examples of poor surface conditions which seriously affect crop establishment in direct drilling are shown in the five plates 16–20. They cover smearing, surface ponding, trash in the drilled slot and the effect of poor burning of trash and straw. Slaking is also a common surface condition in fine sandy loams low in organic matter.

PLATE 13
Medium soil: calcareous loam.   ICI Plant Protection Division

OVERCOMING THE PROBLEMS[,2,5,6]

Surface Problems
Some of the problems mentioned above are inherent in a particular
soil; indeed, they are the reasons for a soil being placed in Category
3, for example. They may be alleviable or irremediable. Adequate
drainage is of course fundamental to the whole matter of soil improvement and is dealt with elsewhere. Surface compaction must
be remedied before any direct drilling is contemplated. If it is very
severe (for instance following a wet and late harvest), then the
wheel rutting is likely to be too severe to permit the use of the
direct drilling technique. Some form of tine cultivation is indicated,
and then only as soil conditions allow. Smearing can be avoided by

PLATE 14
Light soil: sandy soil with 10 per cent organic matter.

ICI Plant Protection Division

endeavouring to direct drill when surface conditions are reasonably dry and friable.

A good straw and stubble 'burn', coupled with early autumn drilling will usually circumvent some of these 'surface' problems. Given a clean burnt stubble, and provided conditions are sufficiently dry, a chain harrow hitched to the direct drill will create a surface tilth. A straight tine cultivator, driven fairly rapidly and designed to disturb the soil to a depth of about 5 cm, can often provide very satisfactory conditions for direct drilling, ensuring more uniform drilling depth. The straight tine, properly used, will break up the soil, leaving the finer crumbs on the surface, whereas the spring tine lifts the soil, allowing the finer crumbs to filter down and leaving the larger aggregates on top.

PLATE 15
Heavy soil: clay loam.   ICI Plant Protection Division

Closing the drill slots is most important, to protect the seed from weather, birds and slugs. On a clean stubble chain harrowing is effective, but on a killed grass sward rolling immediately after direct drilling will close the slots and prevent moisture loss.

Treating Problems in the Deeper Soil Layer
The ideal soil condition for direct drilling is a firm, level surface with continuous cracking to depth. Deep cultivation is not the answer: it will loosen the soil excessively and allow it to compact again very easily; moreover it leaves a very cloddy surface. The trick is to achieve the shattering *at depth* without disturbing surface soil conditions. Considerable progress has been made in this area by the development of the flat 'A' blade, used at Terrington Ex-

PLATE 16
Smeared drill slot: silty clay loam.

ICI Plant Protection Division

PLATE 17
Slaking (surface dispersion): fine sandy loam.

ICI Plant Protection Division

PLATE 18
Surface ponding: clay loam.

ICI Plant Protection Division

perimental Husbandry Farm, and the 'Paraplow', designed and developed by the late Paul Koronka of ICI Plant Protection Division and now manufactured by the Howard Rotavator Company Ltd. The latter implement is described more fully in Chapter 6.

A great advantage of the 'Paraplow' is that it works well even in wet soil, whereas subsoiling when soils are wet will result in poor 'shatter' and moling the subsoil may reduce the risk of waterlogging but will not 'bust' the soil above the mole.

SOIL STRUCTURE IMPROVEMENT UNDER CONTINUOUS DIRECT DRILLING

The effects of continuous direct drilling on concentration gradients of organic matter and nutrients have already been discussed earlier (Chapter 3). The Survey by Gowman and his colleagues[5] covered fields which had been under continuous direct drilling (with cereals) for up to nine years, and they underline three characteristic features of soil after long-term use of the system, viz:

PLATE 19
Trash pressed in drill slot.   ICI Plant Protection Division

1. A marked variation in soil colour down the profile with the darkest soil at the surface.
2. Very active earthworm populations.
3. A modified but porous soil structure.

Colour
The concentration of darker soil near the surface correlates well with the concentration gradient of organic matter, due to lack of soil disturbance resulting in an accumulation of organic matter and plant debris at or near the soil surface. This colour difference is not evident for the first three years.

Earthworms
Earthworm channels are a striking feature of nearly all long-term direct drilled soils. These are produced mainly by *Lumbricus*

PLATE 6
A well-structured calcareous loam representative of a category 1 soil.

PLATE 7
Friable surface tilth and well-structured top soil in a clay which has been direct drilled for three years; representative of a category 2 soil.

PLATE 8
A sandy soil of low organic matter, easily compacted when not disturbed by cultivation and representative of a category 3 soil.

PLATE 20
Effect of poor trash burning.

ICI Plant Protection Division

species (especially *L. terrestris*) and *Allolobophora chlorotica*, which is a surface feeder. The importance of these earthworm channels (in some cases 5 mm in diameter) has been mentioned several times already.

Soil Structure

With the exception of the light limestone brash and the chalk downland soils, where direct drilling did not appear to modify structure, all other soils showed some modification after continuous use of the system, mainly evidenced by greater porosity and better drainage. This was particularly evident on heavier soils.

EFFECT OF LONG-TERM DIRECT DRILLING ON COMPACTION

As a supplement to what has already been said, it is of interest to note that Soane and his colleagues studying compaction at the Scottish Institute of Agricultural Engineering (SIAE) found that following ploughing to 25–30 cm subsequent wheel traffic caused very large recompaction effects throughout the depth of cultivation. In contrast, where direct drilling is adopted the soil rapidly builds up to an equilibrium level of compaction and it then has a high enough strength to resist further compaction. On certain well-structured soils this level of compaction does not restrict crop development unduly, and yields are comparable with those from ploughing. However, these workers warn that on less well-structured soils the same pattern of traffic may result in adverse soil physical conditions and poor yields. They conclude by saying that compactibility is a critical factor in assessing the suitability of a soil for direct drilling.[8]

Soane's observations fit closely with those made by Davies *et al.* in East Anglia in the ADAS long-term experiments summarised in Chapter 2. In general 'good' soils remain satisfactory, presumably because there is the correct balance between 'compacting' and 'loosening' forces, whereas less suitable soils deteriorate whenever the compacting forces become dominant, such as in wet seasons. Three of the clay sites in those trials—Rawreth (London clay), Knapwell (Oxford clay) and Emnett (alluvial clay)—and a sandy clay site have all become overcompacted at various times under continuous direct drilling whereas the chalky boulder clay sites have not overcompacted in any year. The sandy soils in the trial series have degraded readily, but it has been found that on these soils earthworm burrows can restore sufficient coarse porosity, given enough time, if their numbers are sufficiently high. The North Creake site provides a good example of this 'restoration.'[3]

Thus a strong case has been established for direct drilling as a major contribution towards reducing compaction. In papers delivered to a SAWMA Conference at the NCAE at Silsoe, Beds., in February 1981, Soane[9] and Elliott[4] drew attention to the contribution that could be made with low-pressure tyres, multiple wheels, air-cushion vehicles and other load-reducing systems in lessening the risk of soil compaction.

Clearly the possibilities of all of these ideas, in combination with minimal tillage, demand further and urgent exploration not only by agronomists and soil scientists but also by manufacturers of agricultural machinery, vehicles and tyres. What an opportunity for a joint approach presents itself!

REFERENCES

1. CANNELL, R. Q., DAVIES, D. B., MACKNEY, D. and PIDGEON, J. D. (1978), *Outl. Agric.*, **9**, 6, 306–16.
2. DAVIES, D. B., FINNEY, J. B. and EAGLE, D. (1972), *Soil Management*, (Farming Press Ltd, Ipswich).

3. DAVIES, D. B. (1981), Personal communication.
4. ELLIOTT, J. G. (1981), *Paper* to SAWMA Conf. 'Soil Compaction & its Cures', Silsoe, 4 Feb. 1981.
5. GOWMAN, M. A., COUTTS, J. and RILEY, D. (1977), Unpublished *Report*, I.C.I. P. P. Div.
6. GOWMAN, M. A. (1976), *7th Conf. Int. Soil Till. Res. Org.*, Sweden, 1976.
7. MAFF, ADAS (1978), *Cereals Without Ploughing*, Profitable Farm Enterprises Booklet 6, 29–48.
8. SOANE, B. D., PIDGEON, J. D. BLACKWELL, P. S. and DICKSON, J. W. (1977), *Soil & Water*, **5**, 4 (1977), 2–6.
9. SOANE, B. D. (1981), *Paper* to SAWMA Conf., 'Soil Compaction & its Cures', Silsoe, 4 Feb. 1981.
10. WILKINSON, B. D., MAFF, ADAS. E. Midlands (1975) *Outl. Agric.*, **8** (Special No.), 233–5.

Chapter 5

THE INFLUENCE OF DIRECT DRILLING ON THE INCIDENCE OF WEEDS, DISEASES AND PESTS

The intensification of cereal growing, in particular the widespread adoption of long runs of winter cereals, has altered fundamentally the pattern of weed, disease and pest incidence. Monoculture, especially of crops which occupy the ground for most of the year, encourages the spread of perennial weeds, particularly those which propagate vegetatively such as couch grass (*Agropyron repens*), black bent (*Agrostis gigantea*) and creeping bent (*Agrostis stolonifera*). Also encouraged are those annuals which germinate in late autumn, after a winter cereal crop is drilled. Likewise the widescale growing of cereals has resulted in diseases such as mildew (*Erisyphe graminis*), Leaf spot (*Septoria tritici*), Glume blotch (*Septoria nodorum*), Leaf blotch (*Rhynchosporium secalis*) and some rusts (*Puccinia* spp.) increasing both in incidence and importance. Pests incidence has also increased, though perhaps less spectacularly.

Of course, there is available to the farmer a plethora of pesticides with which, by careful selection and use, invaders may be suppressed; indeed, cereal growing could not have developed as it has without such aids. The purpose of this chapter is to examine the influence of alternative cultivations, especially direct drilling, on the incidence of weeds, diseases, and pests, and to consider the extent, if any, to which current crop protection techniques must be modified in direct drilled crops.

INFLUENCE ON WEED INCIDENCE

Annual Broadleaved Weeds
The obvious and fundamental difference between mouldboard

ploughing followed by secondary cultivations, and direct drilling, is that the former involves complete inversion and thorough mixing of the top soil down to 25 cm whereas the latter concerns the absolute minimum of soil disturbance, at most a shallow cultivation of the top 2·5 cm. In between these extremes are the varying degrees and depths of tined cultivation.

The seeds of annual weeds tend to be distributed throughout the top soil by ploughing, whereas they are left very near the surface by direct drilling. Experiments by Pollard and Cussans[7] indicated that, under continuous direct drilling, the number of broadleaved weeds on ploughed land (P) was markedly higher than on direct drilled land (DD); surprisingly, however, the ratio P/DD did not alter significantly during a five-year period, taking all the broad-leaved species present into consideration. This suggests that there must have been very considerable reserves of some of those weeds in the soil, so that although in each individual year under direct drilling less seeds germinated, the total effect on the soil weed population was inconsequential.

Annual Grass Weeds

Wild oats (Avena *spp)*
Earlier work at the Weed Research Organisation had shown that under direct drilling, especially where straw was burnt before sowing the crop, the natural mortality of wild oats (A. *fatua*) was greater than where land was cultivated soon after cereal harvest. This was confirmed in experiments with spring barley[9, 10] where populations of this species of wild oats were reduced under direct drilling compared with ploughing. Conversely, in the Letcombe/ WRO Joint Tillage Project, the wild oat populations were *higher* on direct drilled plots than on ploughed. It is surmised that in the latter experiments the buried seed population of wild oats was very much higher than that of the more recently shed seed, so that the increased mortality of wild oats in the autumn on undisturbed soil was of little relevance. Furthermore, in those experiments the earlier emerging wild oats were able to survive on the direct drilled plots which were not cultivated (nor sprayed) before direct drilling in the spring.

Where winter cereals are direct drilled, the wild oats germinating in the autumn (both A. *ludoviciana* and A. *fatua*) have the potential of being (a) the most serious source of competition to the crop and (b) the source of new seed. Thus the encouragement of autumn germinating wild oat seedlings under direct drilling systems, and particularly where the straw has been burnt, is both a threat and an opportunity. It is a threat in that it provides a potent source of competition with the crop, and an opportunity, because a bigger target is offered for early removal of this competition. Much depends, of course, on the proportion of wild oat seedlings which can be induced to germinate before or very soon after the winter cereal crop is drilled. At Drayton EHF where the main species of wild oat is the autumn germinating A. *ludoviciana* they claim considerable success in controlling this weed with their system of burning stubbles (after cultivating headlands) followed by two or more passes with a spring-tine cultivator in late August/early September, with a final pre-drilling cultivation (or a spray with a low rate of paraquat if conditions are wet) just before drilling the cereal early in October.

Blackgrass (Alopecurus myosuroides)
Experiments at WRO and elsewhere have demonstrated increased populations of this weed under reduced cultivation and direct drilling systems. However, its extended germination pattern makes it a potential problem in continuous winter cereal enterprises irrespective of the method of cultivation employed, especially in those areas (such as East and South-East England) where it is more prevalent. It used to be said of blackgrass that it germinated in 'flushes' throughout the autumn; in fact it is capable of germinating in autumn, early winter and early spring. So this seriously competitive grass weed must be monitored with the utmost vigilance and attacked promptly whatever the cultivation system under which the winter cereal crop is grown.

Sterile (or Barren) brome-grass (Bromus sterilis)
This weed, known for many years but not considered important, has burst into prominence during the past five years, and is now looked upon as a potential menace. It was always assumed that sterile brome seeds possessed little or no dormancy, that the vast majority of its seed germinated in the autumn, and that the seed did not persist for long in the soil as a viable entity. It now appears that these assumptions can all be challenged. It has been suggested that the increased area of winter cereals, reduced cultivations/direct drilling *and* earlier drilling, have all contributed to the spread of this weed. It must be tackled in the headlands, before it moves into the field.

Various views have been advanced concerning the suppression of sterile brome-grass. It is suggested that a good 'burn' following harvest will at least kill some of the 'shed' seed. Further, if sterile brome is known to be present in a field where direct drilling of a winter cereal is planned, a very light cultivation (especially around the headlands) is advised to encourage germination. If paraquat or glyphosate are applied to control stubble weeds before sterile brome has emerged it will prosper against greatly reduced competition. Metoxuron and tri-allate have proved reasonably effective against this weed but the latter requires careful incorporation and is therefore not compatible with 'strict' direct drilling. Further mention of this weed is made in the case studies in Chapter 8.

INFLUENCE ON THE EFFICIENCY OF PRE-EMERGENCE HERBICIDES

As this aspect concerns treatment of annual grass and broadleaved weeds, it is discussed here before considering perennial weeds.

There is no doubt that direct drilling, especially when practised for a number of years, leads to increased amounts of organic matter in the surface soil, as described in Chapter 3. This result of direct drilling is without doubt beneficial. At the same time, it is well known that certain herbicides applied to soil pre-crop emergence may be rendered less effective in the presence of soil organic matter; indeed, it is implicit in the manufacturers' recommendations of the pre-emergence application of many herbicides. This is not a 'fault' of direct drilling; it is however, a factor of which careful note must be taken both by those framing recommendations, by advisers and by farmers. Often an early post-emergence treatment with an appropriate herbicide on soils which have been direct drilled for some years provides a solution to the problem.

Perennial Grass Weeds

Couch grass (Agropyron repens)
This pernicious weed requires no detailed description. Capable of producing extensive rhizomes which can ramify quickly through the topsoil, it can exploit any weakness in crop growth and occupy any untenanted area in the field. It can exist under conditions unfavourable to most crop plants, lurk surreptitiously in a grass sward ready to proliferate once the grass is replaced by an arable crop, and even add insult to injury by exuding toxins into the soil to threaten plants in close proximity! Under any system of farming it is a serious potential enemy—under intensive winter cereal runs, it

can be most dangerous and, as a broad generalisation, it must be conceded that reduced cultivation and direct drilling systems can offer maximum opportunity for the weed to flourish. Of this weed it can be said, with feeling, that the price of liberty (i.e. freedom from the weed) is constant vigilance.

In the orthodox rotational systems of the past the opportunity to deal with couch grass was in the root crops with inter-row cultivation and especially in the autumn before a spring cereal—indeed, both full fallows and bastard fallows were adopted with the main objective of coping with the weed. Advice given for couch-grass control forty years ago was to loosen the plants by ploughing, then drag them to the surface by repeated cultivations, draggings and spring tooth harrowings; roll up rhizomes with chain harrows then either burn or cart off. This would be followed by more ploughing to bring up deeper rhizomes and dragging again. A 'smother' crop, i.e. potatoes, would then follow to complete the process.

Since those days herbicides such as dalapon and amino-triazole have played an important part against couch but always in tandem with some form of deep cultivation.

The advent of reduced cultivation systems, in particular direct drilling, produced situations ideal for the growth and spread of couch grass—an undisturbed soil carrying a crop which in its earlier stages of growth could provide no satisfactory competition. This was evident from early trials by ICI and by ADAS but notably where two conditions prevailed. There was, firstly, a nucleus of couch grass present and secondly the soil was poorly drained and/or waterlogged, leading to failure or partial failure of direct drilled crops. Under the latter conditions creeping bent, blackgrass, and grass weeds also thrived at the expense of the crop. Indeed, in a long-term experiment at WRO, the growth of couch rhizomes on direct drilled plots was very many times greater than on plots cultivated in September and ploughed in December. The rhizomes under direct drilled plots were also produced at a much shallower depth than on ploughed plots.

It was not surprising that couch grass should take hold in the situation described above and it was essential to counter the problem. The first step was to counsel that fields selected for direct drilling should be free from couch grass and other creeping perennial grasses. This was, and still is, good advice because, even today, with better weapons at hand (i.e. glyphosate), it makes sounder sense to plan ahead and eliminate, or at least reduce severely, the threat from the grass before moving into a direct drilling system.

Paraquat is not a couch-killer. It will deal effectively with the aerial growth but new shoots will soon appear. Used in very small doses (0·7 litres/ha of the commercial product) each time couch grass shoots reach a height of about 5 cm, paraquat can reduce couch growth quite appreciably, but such an approach may be practised successfully only where a spring crop is to be direct drilled. Glyphosate used at 4 litres/ha of the commercial product will suppress the weed effectively.

There are two basic requirements for successful suppression of couch grass by glyphosate. First, there must be adequate growth of the weed and second, there must be dry weather for at least six hours, preferably 24 hours, after application. This can pose a problem in a dry autumn where there may not be much stubble vegetation available as a target; in addition, straw burning will reduce the leaf area of couch available for spraying, thus delaying the operation. On the other hand, in a wet autumn the six-hour dry period may prove elusive. Furthermore, where harvest is delayed until late September, the date at which couch reaches the stage where it is susceptible to glyphosate *may* coincide with a low-temperature induced dormancy which lessens the movement of herbicide within the couch plant. The manufacturers of glyphosate are now recommending treatment of couch grass at the time when new rhizome is produced and the weed is growing actively, that is, before the harvest of the wheat and barley. They claim that this treatment also suppresses late developing cereal tillers and annual weeds, helping to facilitate harvesting.

It may well be that the best way to cope with couch grass and to embark on direct drilling free from its menace, is to deal with couch as recommended with glyphosate but in a conventionally drilled cereal first.

Bent grasses

Black Bent (Agrostis gigantea) is a rhizomatous perennial, rather like couch in its habit though not by any means as widespread. What has been written about 'true' couch (*Agropyron repens*) will hold for black bent.

Creeping Bent or water grass (*Agrostis stolonifera*) develops via surface stems or stolons from which adventitious roots and shoots are produced at intervals. Like couch, it can tolerate a range of surface conditions including poor drainage and waterlogging. So it will soon proliferate in such situations to the further detriment of an already stricken crop; that is, if it is allowed to thrive and expand in the first place. Indeed, on heavier and wetter soils it can often be more common than couch grass. Clearly, if creeping bent is present, and not suppressed at the outset, conditions involving no soil disturbance will favour its spread.

As with couch and black bent therefore, creeping bent should be tackled before direct drilling is planned. Paraquat and glyphosate are very effective against creeping bent when applied in the autumn, but good coverage of the weed by the spray is essential.

Perennial Broadleaved Weeds (docks, dandelions, creeping thistle etc.)

As with perennial grass weeds, these tap-rooted perennials thrive if left alone, but docks in particular, especially the broadleaved dock (*Rumex obtusifolius*) also burgeon if they are chopped up and spread by cultivation. There are herbicides available to control such weeds (e.g. glyphosate, asulam and mecoprop) and recommendations on manufacturers' labels should be followed. As with couch and the bents, deal with these weeds *before* embarking upon direct drilling regime.

In this category unwanted white clover may be considered as a weed—if clover is present in quantity in a sward glyphosate should be applied before direct drilling.

INFLUENCE ON DISEASE INCIDENCE

Observations of the influence of direct drilling on foliar and root diseases of cereals have been made throughout the period of development of the technique. For example, in 1963–4 it was noted in the trials at Jealott's Hill, especially in the first direct drilling experiment (CP1), that the incidence of take-all (*Gaeumannomyces graminis*) was lower in direct drilled plots than in the cultivated plots (see later).[4] From 1970 onwards studies of the effects of cultivation treatments on disease incidence in cereals have been conducted by ADAS, Rothamsted Experimental Station in conjunction with NIAE, and by Edinburgh and East of Scotland College of Agriculture. These researches, and the various interpretations placed on their results, are described by Yarham.[11] He cites three factors governing the severity of disease in the crop: (1) the amount of inoculum of the pathogen available to initiate the epidemic, (2) the susceptibility of the 'host' plants, and (3) the suitability of the environment for spread of the pathogen and the infection of the host. Yarham also examined the way in which the changes from ploughing to direct drilling may influence these three factors with respect to the major pathogens of intensive cereal cropping.

Effect of 'Non-Plough' Systems on Initial Levels of Inoculum

1. On green plant material

In a direct drilling system, although it is perfectly feasible to kill 'volunteer' cereals with a herbicide such as paraquat, climatic conditions in the autumn may delay the germination of some plants. The result may be that live volunteers, which can harbour rusts, mildew or virus diseases escape the spray so that these diseases are already present in the newly drilled winter cereal. Likewise, the greater likelihood of survival of couch grass in direct drilled crops may bring with it the added hazard of take-all which can be carried by couch grass. Furthermore, if blackgrass is allowed to build up in a continuous direct drilling sequence of winter cereals, it could increase risk of infection of ergot (*Claviceps purpurea*) in wheat.

2. On dead plant debris

Eyespot (*Pseudocercosporella herpotrichoides*), leaf spot and glume blotch of wheat, leaf blotch and net blotch (*Pyrenophora teres*) of barley can exist on dead plant residues and are not affected by herbicides, although the burning of straw will reduce the incidence of some of these.

Take-all presents a more complex picture, because changes in husbandry, by modifying root distribution, may influence the extent of attack, not only on surface roots but deeper down.

Effects of Factors Associated with Direct Drilling on the Susceptibility of the Crop

Yarham refers to the effect of time of sowing as an influential factor. Early drilled winter crops, emerging while autumn temperatures are relatively high, may be vulnerable to foliar pathogens (such as mildew) still active at that time, whereas later sown crops are likely to escape this hazard. The tendency towards slower establishment of autumn-sown direct drilled cereals (compared with those sown into more orthodox seedbeds) may result in a lower incidence of disease, however. Brooks and Dawson working at Jealott's Hill[2] drew this inference from their study, which showed higher levels of eyespot on ploughed plots; results at Boxworth EHF on winter barley in 1975 appear to confirm this view.

Interactions between cultivation treatments and nutrient levels have already been described (Chapter 3). Differences in levels and distribution of nutrients in 'non-ploughing' systems, in particular under direct drilling, may be expected to influence susceptibility of crops to disease, but there is no clear-cut or consistent relationship. Shipton (then with ADAS based at Reading)[8] studied nitrogen/ disease interaction in commercial-scale field trials in Hampshire. However, he failed to find any effect of different N levels on either take-all or eyespot in winter wheat and barley sown into stubble by *traditional* methods. There seems no justification for believing that the situation would be different had the cereals been direct drilled, although in Scotland[6] increase in N rates was found to reduce incidence of take-all infection.

Pests such as wireworms, insofar as they may damage cereal roots and thereby facilitate the entry of root pathogens, e.g. leaf-stripe of wheat (*Cephalosporium gramineum*) can influence disease levels in some instances, so the extent to which the pest attack is affected by cultivation systems may have an indirect influence on disease levels.

In the ADAS Eastern Region experimental series with winter wheat (see Chapter 2) the following conclusions were drawn for the period 1971–5:

● That in twenty-four experiments and field observation studies completed during that period, whilst there were high levels of *Septoria* in direct drilled winter wheat, the disease did not develop.

● That there were no consistent differences in the development of take-all or eyespot.

● That no case was encountered where poor yield in non-ploughed areas was attributed to the effects of these cultivation techniques on disease levels.

Effects on soil microflora may in turn influence the incidence of certain soil-borne diseases. This has been demonstrated by Brooks[1] and by Brooks & Dawson[2] whose work indicated greater microbial activity in direct drilled soil. They suggested that some of these microbial organisms (e.g. *Phialophora radicicola*, which is often present in old grassland) are antagonistic to both take-all and eyespot. Certainly in the long-term experiment at Jealott's Hill[4] take-all levels in 1964 were very much lower and crop yields very much higher on direct drilled plots than in ploughed plots (2·6% take-all under direct drilling and 20·4% under ploughing). Such clear differences have been rare, however.

To sum up, from evidence up to the present it can be said that though certain diseases may be increased by moving away from ploughing, this has not been accompanied by depressed crop yields. It does not seem likely that interaction between cultivation treatment and disease levels will have significant influence on the success or failure of non-ploughing systems.

Careful monitoring and the sensible use of fungicides are advised, especially against the trash-borne diseases which *may* increase under non-ploughing, i.e. those which survive on plant debris on the soil surface (*Rhynchosporium*, *Septoria*, and *Pseudocercosporella*).

INFLUENCE ON PEST INCIDENCE

Observations of the effects of 'no-plough' cultivations and direct drilling on soil fauna generally have been undertaken at Rothamsted.[3] This work covers arthropods, earthworms, slugs, and wireworms. Other work on slugs has been reported[5] and there have been many observations from experiments, from developmental trials and from commercial direct drilling concerning slugs in particular. The only other pest to have received close attention in the context of direct drilling is the frit-fly (*Oscinella frit*).

General effects on arthropods
Whilst the numbers of mites and springtails were greater on undisturbed soil than on ploughed and cultivated land, insect populations, particularly larvae of *Diptera* (flies), and some beetles (e.g. carabids) tended to be greater on ploughed land. The larger numbers of mites and springtails under direct drilling are considered an advantage because they feed on decaying plant residues, so helping to break them down and incorporate them into the subsoil.

Earthworms
Reference was made in Chapter 3 to Letcombe results. These are corroborated by the Rothamsted experiments which show that populations of *Lumbricus terrestris* were two and a half to five times more numerous on direct drilled plots (see Table 30).

Other earthworm species were slightly more numerous under direct drilling.

Wireworms
Rothamsted's findings were that wireworms were two to three times more numerous on direct drilled plots. Edwards surmised that this was due to the fact that mechanical cultivations may cause physical damage to wireworms, *or* may bury them, *or* bring them to the surface to be eaten by birds.[3] There is no record of this having

Table 30. Earthworm populations in three experiments

		Number in field quadrats		
Group	Site	Direct drilled	Ploughed	Ratio $\frac{D/D}{P}$
Lumbricus	Woburn	323	103	3·14
terrestris	Rothamsted	61	25	2·44
	Boxworth	22	4	5·50
Other	Woburn	1315	1140	1·15
Species	Rothamsted	858	603	1·42
	Boxworth	789	663	1·19

(Source: After C A Edwards, Rothamsted, 1975) (Ref. 3)

serious consequences in commercial direct drilling. Indeed, in recent years, wireworms do not appear to have been a serious threat to cereal crops; possibly the widespread use of seed treatments containing insecticides has been partly responsible.

Slugs

In the early experiments involving direct drilling, wherever trash, particularly straw, was left on the soil surface, and especially in a wet autumn, it was found to harbour slugs in large numbers. This obviously created a serious hazard for the direct drilled seeds and seedlings, which was compounded if the slots formed by direct drilling were left open, thereby providing the voracious molluscs with a motorway to feeding points at regular intervals! In the strict sense, therefore, direct drilling can create opportunities for increased slug damage, but if straw is burnt and the direct drilled slots covered, the actual hazard need not be materially greater under direct drilling than under traditional cultivations. Assuredly, however, great care must be taken to do the direct drilling job properly, and with direct drilled brassica crops in particular the use of slug pellets is advised as routine.

Frit-fly

This will be dealt with in more detail in Chapter 8 where we deal with the grass crop. Suffice it to say at this stage that under direct-drilling systems the third generation of frit-fly, which would normally be feeding below ground on decaying organic matter and roots, is feeding near the surface on the killed trash. This may result in a greater hazard, particularly to the newly sown grass and cereal, than under conventional cultivations.

REFERENCES

1. BROOKS, D. H. (1967), *Proc. 4th Brit. Insect & Fung. Conf.*, 1967, 92–5.
2. BROOKS, D. H. and DAWSON, M. G. (1968), *Ann. Appl. Biol*, **61**, 57–64.
3. EDWARDS, C. A. (1975), *Outl. Agric.*, **8** (Special No.) 243–4.
4. HOOD, A. E. M., SHARP, D. G. and COTTERELL, R. (1964), *Proc. 7th B.W.C.C.*, 1964, 907–12.
5. JESSOP, N. H. (1977), *MAFF, ADAS Expt. Dev. Rep. S.E. Region (Arable)*, 1977, 40–1.
6. LOCKHART, D. A. G., HEPPEL, V. A. F. and HOLMES, J. C. (1975), *Edin. Sch. Agric. EPPO Bull.*, 1975, **5** (4), 375–83.
7. POLLARD, F. and CUSSANS, G. W. (1976), *Proc. B.C.P.C. Conf.* (Weeds), 1976, 1001–8.
8. SHIPTON, P. J. (1972), *Pl. Path.*, 1972, **21**, 147–55.
9. WILSON, B. J. (1972), *Proc. 11th B.W.C.C.* (1972), 242–7.
10. WILSON, B. J. and CUSSANS, G. W. (1972), *Proc. 11th B.W.C.C.* (1972), 234–41.
11. YARHAM, D. J. (1975), *Outl. Agric.*, **8** (Special No.), 245–7.

Chapter 6

THE DEVELOPMENT OF MACHINERY FOR DIRECT DRILLING

SPECIALISED DIRECT DRILLS

The critical field experiments of the early 1960s, based at ICI's Jealott's Hill Research Station were carried out with the aid of the JEC 'Grasslands' Sod Seeder, imported from Australia. This was a combined sprayer–seeder and its major shortcomings were the soil-working components, in particular the large shoe-type coulters which ripped large divots out of the sprayed sward. Incidentally, experience also showed that for narrow-spaced crops like cereals the combination of sprayer with seeder had nothing of advantage to offer. These experiments were followed by farm-scale development trials throughout England in 1963 and 1964. In this early work co-operating farmers used their own seed drills for the direct drilling operation, with results which, like the curate's egg, were good in parts!

It was very evident from these farmer trials that the seed drills built for conventional sowing into cultivated soil had two major shortcomings in the context of direct drilling. First, they lacked the ability to penetrate, especially in heavier soils and, second, those drills fitted with 'dished' discs, if they *did* penetrate the surface soil (especially a grass sward) placed the cereal seeds under a 'lip' of soil, making emergence of the seedling a very difficult manoeuvre. It was quite obvious that for direct drilling, major improvements were necessary and the machinery department of ICI Plant Protection Division (then Plant Protection Ltd) took this on as a major research project.

After detailed evaluation of all available coulter systems the 'disc-and-knife' coulter was selected as the simplest system capable of being fitted to existing drills. This consisted of a flat disc, designed to cut through any trash and make the initial slit in the soil to the required depth. Directly behind the disc, and attached to the same member, there followed a foot-shaped knife with a seed boot attached. The knife opened the cut made by the disc and deposited the seed into the soil. Prototype drills using the disc-and-knife coulter system were constructed on Massey Ferguson (MF) 732 drills with specially lowered sub-frames for both mounted and trailed models.

On a number of selected sites results were achieved with these units which were comparable with those from conventional drilling. When the prototypes were used more widely, however, it became evident that blockage by loose straw and trash was a problem, and when soil conditions were hard the knife points wore rapidly, with consequent reduced penetration. Furthermore, in moist conditions the coulter produced polished and smeared slits. The project went back to the drawing board, and as a result of design research led by the late Mr Paul Koronka of ICI, with co-operation from Massey Ferguson Limited, there emerged the all-rolling coulter which came to be known as the triple-disc system. This consisted of a single straight disc set vertically (to open the drill slit) followed by double discs set in a 'V'. The double discs have a rolling action; they expand the slit and the seed is deposited into the slit between them. With these heavier coulters a conversion kit for existing drills was no longer a practical proposition, and a prototype purpose-built drill was produced which incorporated not only the new coulters but superior springing to give improved contour following.

Between 1966 and 1970 a number of manufacturers produced batches of 'triple disc' direct drills and these were hired to contractors to satisfy the needs of farmers who wanted to try the technique but were not at that stage prepared to commit themselves to the purchase of a machine.

Another development aimed at producing a direct drill for grass and forage crops was the conversion of the Howard Rotavator to the 'Rotaseeder' (see plate 21), a joint project between Howards and ICI (Plant Protection Ltd). Basically the modification involved shortening the flanges of the 'L' rotavator blades, so that instead of effecting overall cultivation they cut slots about 2.5 cm wide in soil or sward. The other modification was to fit a seedbox and seedtubes which guide the seed into the slots created by the truncated 'L' blades.

This machine was marketed successfully in the late 1960s, mainly because the direct drilling of kale 'took off', especially by contractors in the South-West. The 'Rotaseeder' proved ideal for small-

PLATE 21
'Rotaseeder' direct drilling cereals into stubble sprayed previously with
Gramoxone.   ICI

acreage work for small dairy farmers whose labour and machinery
were inadequate for them to carry out such operations themselves.

Concurrently with the development of the Rotaseeder, Har-
greaves of Macclesfield and Plant Protection Ltd co-operated in development work with their 'Sisis' Contravator. This machine,
already in use for re-seeding sports grounds and recreation areas,
was also based on a rotary cultivator, but the 'rotation' was in the
opposite direction to that of the Howard machine (that is, against
the direction of travel).

During the late 1960s International Harvester Ltd introduced
from Australia their IH 6–2 cultivator drill (more recently re-
named IH 511). Although this was not specifically aimed at direct
drilling it soon became evident that, on the chalk soils of Wiltshire
and on the brash soils of the Cotswolds in particular, this new drill
was quite capable of direct drilling *and* drilling after 'no-plough'
cultivations.

By 1970, therefore, three main direct drilling machine types
were available for commercial development: .

● The triple-disc system on a strengthened frame.

● The cultivator (tined) drill.
● The powered, modified rotary cultivator drill.
Commercial machines based on these designs and currently available in the UK are described below.

Triple Disc Drills
The Bettinson DD Drill (plate 22)
A combine seed and fertiliser drill, manufactured by Hestair Bettinson Ltd. and designed primarily for direct drilling, but capable of drilling a wide range of seeds under reduced cultivation and conventional systems. Penetration is achieved by means of double-acting hydraulic cylinders which bear down upon a massive pressure beam. Three-metre and 4-metre machines are available, each with 'normal' and 'narrow' row spacing. Thus there are four drills from which to choose: 17 rows (3 metres – 175 mm), 23 rows (4 metres – 175 mm), 24 rows (3 metres – 121 mm) or 32 rows (4 metres – 121 mm).

PLATE 22
Direct drilling cereals into stubble with the Hestair Bettinson DD drill.   ICI

The MF 130 Drill (plate 23).
Introduced by Massey Ferguson Ltd in 1978, this is also a combine

drill capable of direct drilling and of sowing into tine-cultivated and traditionally prepared land. Like the Bettinson machine, it can drill a wide range of seeds, and it employs double-acting hydraulic rams to achieve penetration. The MF 130 is available in two forms—a 15 row (175 mm) machine either combine or grain-only and a 19 row (131 mm) drill, grain only.

Cultivator Drills

The International 511 Cultivator Drill (plate 24)
This machine, like the two triple-disc machines already mentioned, can be used for direct drilling, and for drilling following reduced cultivations or traditional ploughing and cultivation. The tines are sprung and arranged in four rows with a substantial clearance between rows. They are mounted on 'floats' to give better contour-following. Sixteen and 20-row versions are available, each drilling at a row spacing of 180 mm. It is, of course, a combine drill.

ADVANTAGES AND LIMITATIONS

1. Triple Disc Drills
There is no doubt that the triple-disc system works well in a wide range of situations; it is equally certain that when used to direct drill in wet conditions the triple-disc coulters tend to smear (see Chapter 2 page 40). This has been evident not only in the autumn but also in spring where the surface of the soil is drying and the soil just below is still moist. This point must be borne very much in mind. Hestair Bettinson did offer tine coulter sets as accessories at one stage so that users could change over should circumstances demand.

Another slight shortcoming (in the author's view) not only of the triple-disc but of all 'slit seeding' systems is that they are ideal for direct drilling grass into cereal stubble but they have limitations when they are required to drill grass into grass. This is because they do not provide, in a killed sward, the mini tilth produced by such *slot* seeders as the 'Rotaseeder' which is so conducive to consistent, satisfactory germination. This said, clearly the larger triple-disc drills, able to cover a large area each day and to drill a range of seeds, offer what is required by major cereal growers and by con-tractors.

2. Cultivator (tined) Drills
These are less likely to smear but they can rake loose trash and

PLATE 23
The Massey-Ferguson MF 130 direct drill.

ICI Plant Protection Division

PLATE 24
The International 511 cultivator drill.

ICI Plant Protection Division

those machines fitted with forward facing tines tend to dig themselves in, whilst those with solid tines lack flexibility. Most suitable are the spring tines as fitted to the International 511 drill for example.

3. Powered Drills

Brief mention has already been made of the 'Rotaseeder'. The slot-forming property of the 'Rotaseeder' has already been cited as a decided benefit, on lowland and on hill. As a powered tool, it has obvious advantages. On the debit side, its contour-following leaves much to be desired. It will drill cereals but, because of its limited size it is too slow and expensive, and cannot compete with such drills as the Bettinson DD, the MF 130 and the IH 511 in the major cereal-growing areas. The Rotaseeder is a grain-only drill.

Other Drills

The Newcastle Drill (available as the Tasker Direct Drill)
Mention has already been made of the tendency of triple-disc coulters to produce smeared slots when used in wet soil. The Department of Agricultural Engineering at the University of Newcastle upon Tyne took the view that there would be some advantage in a machine capable of causing greater disturbance of the soil *above* the depth of seeding, thereby reducing the risk of a smeared slot and they produced a prototype drill with a seed coulter consisting of a single dished disc, which produces a strip of loosened soil 5 – 8 cm wide into which the seed is deposited. They called this machine the 'Newcastle' drill. Depth control is achieved by attaching a skid to each individual coulter.

This drill was compared with the triple-disc machine at Letcombe Laboratory in 1977 and 1978 on two soils, a silt loam and a clay loam. In 1977, general differences in drill performance were slight with winter oats, but with spring oats on the clay loam the Newcastle drill produced higher yields. In 1978 no differences were apparent.

The drill is now manufactured by Craven Tasker (Andover) Ltd.

The Hayflake 3-metre Direct Drill (plate 25)
During the late 1960s there was a strongly held view that the triple-disc drills then being developed were likely only to be attractive to the very big farm enterprise centred on cereals, and to the contractor; that the Rotaseeder, though excellent, had its limitations, and that a cheaper farmer's drill was needed. One such drill, which was

designed and proffered to meet this need was a hybrid incorporating the Triple-K (Kongskilde) cultivator with the Bamford Octopus Seeder mounted on top. This drill is now available as the Hayflake 3 metre Direct Drill (plate 25). The basis of the drill is still the Kongskilde S tine, each tine independently spring-loaded, and the seeding system is based on a centrifugal unit driven by two trailed land-wheels. It has the advantage of a tine drill in that it is less likely to cause smearing than triple discs if used to direct drill in wet top soil; on the other hand, like other cultivator drills, it tends to rake loose trash.

The Moore Uni-Drill (plate 26)
This grain-only drill is a development of the mid-1970s. A narrow row-spacing direct drill, claimed to be suitable for grass, brassica crops and cereals, it is an 18-coulter machine, drilling at 120 mm row width. There are nine drag-arm seeding units, each with two discs with two press wheel-rollers (one in line with and behind each disc), spring mounted to the main frame of the drill. The discs are mounted at opposite angles on either side of each drag-arm and a seed-tube coulter is mounted on the inner side of each disc, so that the seed is deposited in the slit cut by the discs. The press wheel-rollers close the soil around the seed in the slit. This produces a reasonable tilth on the surface if used when the soil is sufficiently dry to be friable.

The Moore All-Till Uni-Drill
This is now available commercially. Also an 18-coulter machine, it drills at 166 mm. It is a 3-metre drill and the seed-box capacity, at 600 litres, is almost twice that of the original Uni-Drill.

The Gibbs Direct Drill (plate 27)
This was originally designed for direct drilling brassica crops. There are two models, the 6-row machine drilling at 30 cm centres and the contractors' 7-row machine, drilling at 35 cm centres, with a capability of drilling four rows at 70 cm centres. Bolted to each seed coulter is a hardened point with winged plates which help to keep open the slit until the seed is deposited from the hopper. The machine will also drill maize or beans, using the deeper drilling point.

The Mil-Aitchison Seed-Matic 1000
The Aitchison drill, manufactured in New Zealand, is now sold in the United Kingdom by Mil Ltd. A 16-coulter drill sowing at 150

PLATE 25
The Hayflake 3-metre direct drill.

ICI Plant Protection Division

PLATE 26
The Moore Uni-Drill.

ICI

PLATE 27
The Gibbs direct drill.

ICI

mm row widths, this is designed especially to direct drill grass into grass but has also a wide seed-drilling range (0.25 – 90 kg/ha). It is fitted with spring steel tines and has alternative coulters, one designed for slicing through turf, the other, a wedge coulter, for use in cultivated soil.

There are numerous other direct drills but the foregoing are those most readily available on the UK market in 1981.

A number of direct drills are manufactured and used overseas, among them the Gaspardo single-grain seeder, a precision maize direct drill, manufactured in Italy and the Duncan 730 Multi-seeder, a triple disc drill made in New Zealand. There is also the Nodet drill made in France.

Thus the farmer has now available a range of versatile drills designed so that they may direct drill but capable also of drilling into shallow cultivated soils and traditionally ploughed and cultivated land. For further information the interested farmer will obviously seek advice from machinery manufacturers.

CULTIVATORS FOR 'ALTERNATIVE CULTIVATIONS'

In the main, farmers seeking planting systems which avoid the mouldboard plough have resorted to commercially available cultivators. Some have arrived at the cultivation system of their choice by trial and rejection until they have found what they want. For example, at Drayton EHF they started with large chisel ploughs, and eventually settled on a 'Flexitine'. Mr Rex Jenkinson uses a Scandinavian C tine cultivator to produce the scratch tilth he desires before direct drilling (see Chapter 8). Mr John Muirhead (see Chap. 13) has designed his own machine, the Progressive Cultivator, for soil disturbance from the surface down to the subsoil—maximal rather than minimal cultivation but without inversion. Other machines like the Tasker Power Harrow are also capable of producing a scratch tilth.

The aim of 'no-plough' cultivation, as distinct from direct drilling, is to achieve a suitable seedbed with minimal compaction and adequate aeration, whilst preserving, as far as possible, the vertical communication afforded by pores, fissures, earthworm channels and root channels in soils. It is up to the farmer to determine what implement or modification of an implement suits him best. Provided he is aware of the soil management he must achieve, he will find what he seeks through trial and error—it is certainly not possible to write a recipe for the ideal cultivator for each farmer or each soil type.

Soil Loosening at Depth on Land to be Direct Drilled

Provided that soil conditions are right and that guidelines have been followed, direct drilling can be practised with consistent success and has much to offer. In less favourable conditions of soil and climate, however, or when management is less skilful, direct drilling might well result in lower yields. For example, on soils of unstable structure, rain may cause slaking and compaction; direct drilling under less than ideal conditions on such soils may result in smearing, smeared slits and compacted wheelings.

In Chapter 4 methods of determining suitability of soil types (and conditions) for direct drilling were outlined, and guidance was given concerning the recognition of soil problems and of some ways of dealing with them when they had been identified.

As in most operations connected with the soil, experience and judgement on the part of the farmer are all-important, but there are ways in which certain defects which render a soil unsuitable for direct drilling are remediable. Drainage, moling and subsoiling

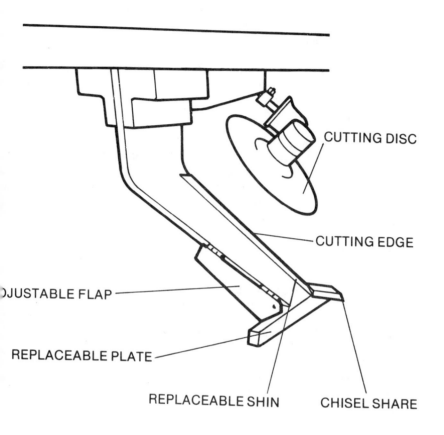

CUTTING DISC

CUTTING EDGE

ADJUSTABLE FLAP

REPLACEABLE PLATE

REPLACEABLE SHIN

CHISEL SHARE

Fig. 7. A 'Paraplow' leg.

ICI Plant Protection Division

have been mentioned already in the context of preparing land for direct drilling. We are concerned here with improving soil conditions lower down, whilst retaining the firm, level surface required for successful direct drilling—*assuming that the underdrainage has been put right.*

ICI have always been concerned to extend their guidelines for direct drilling to cover a wider range of soil *conditions*. This was a preoccupation of the late Paul Koronka—whose considerable contribution to the development of direct drilling, in particular direct drilling machinery, is acknowledged here—and his work and that of his colleagues led to the development of the machine now manufactured by Howard Rotavator Co Ltd as the 'Paraplow'. The development trials with the implement provide encouraging evidence of its ability to achieve a deep loosening of the soil, destruction of plough plans and relief of compaction without losing the advantage of a firm, level, undisturbed soil surface.

The 'Paraplow' (plates 28 and 29)
At first glance (see fig. 7) the 'Paraplow' is similar to a slant-legged subsoiler, but:
- it incorporates cutting discs in front of each leg, enabling it to work through heavy trash or any form of surface mulch;
- each slant leg has a replaceable leading tip;
- an adjustable flap behind each leg makes it possible to regulate the amount of soil disturbance produced.

When it is desired to produce maximum loosening of the soil, it is possible to fit a levelling device behind each leg to maintain a firm, level surface whilst achieving 'crack'. Figure 8 shows what happens to the soil when the 'Paraplow' passes through.

It is claimed that the 'Paraplow' will extend considerably the range of soil conditions under which direct drilling may be carried out successfully, and in 1981 the implement is being subjected to further wide-scale field testing.

The NIAE Tasker Tillage Train
This particular system for preparing a seed-bed by minimal tillage consists of a tine cultivator and disc harrow combined into a single machine. As the title indicates it is a development of NIAE and Messrs Tasker. It can cultivate fully the top 5 cm of soil across the full width of the three-metre machine in one high-speed pass, leaving the soil ready for drilling with either a combine or grain-

PLATE 28
The Howard 'Paraplow' – out of work.

ICI Plant Protection Division

PLATE 29
The Howard 'Paraplow' – in work.

ICI Plant Protection Division

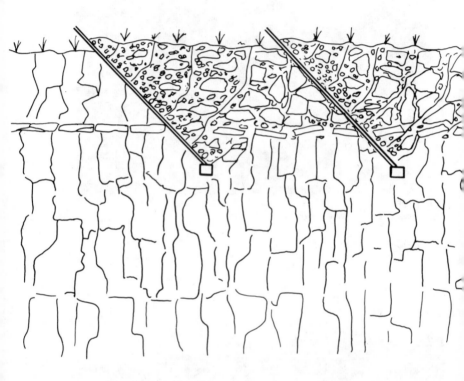

Fig. 8. Effect of using 'Paraplow' soil loosener.   ICI Plant Protection Division

only drill. Any weeds that are encouraged to germinate by this cultivation can be dealt with either by a second pass with the 'train' at right angles to the first pass, or by spraying with a low dose of paraquat.

The tillage train can work at rate of 3 hectares per hour. It requires a four-wheel drive tractor with a power output of 100 hp on light soils and 140 hp on heavier soils. Craven Tasker (Andover) Ltd, Agricultural Division, will supply further details.

Chapter 7

THE ECONOMIC CASE

The object of this chapter is to outline and discuss the predominant economic benefits of direct drilling and of 'no-plough' cultivations, and to attempt to answer from the economic viewpoint the question, 'Why consider direct drilling?'

ECONOMIC ADVANTAGES

In a paper give to a Conference at Stoneleigh in March 1979, Mr T. W. D. Theophilus of ADAS Eastern Region[5] summarised the economic advantages of direct drilling as he saw them. He compared production costs of the technique with reduced cultivations and with traditional ploughing, using 1978 standard costings. His figures are given in Table 31.

Table 31. Comparative costs of drilling a crop (£ per hectare)

Direct drilling		*Reduced cultivation*		*Traditional ploughing*	
Operation	*Cost*	*Operation*	*Cost*	*Operation*	*Cost*
Spray materials 2·8 l/ha	13.00	3-tine cultivations	24.70	Ploughing	20.32
Spraying	3.20	Spray materials	6.50	Two discings	14.10
Harrowing	4.10	Spraying	3.20	Spray materials	3.25
Drill hire	20.00	Harrowing	4.10	Spraying	3.20
		Drilling	6.10	Harrowing	4.10
				Drilling	6.10
TOTAL	£40.30	TOTAL	£44.60	TOTAL	£51.07

(Source: after Theophilus, ADAS Cambridge, 1979) (Ref. 5)

This table indicates a cost saving of £11 per hectare by adopting direct drilling assuming the job was done by a contractor. For the farmer owning his own direct drill the saving would be much greater. This assumes, also, a moderately low dosage rate of herbicide, which may have to be increased, depending on the severity of

PLATE 30
Frit fly damage on direct drilled winter wheat.

PLATE 31
An area in the same field as photo 30 protected by an insecticide (pirimphos methyl 'Blex' by ICI).

PLATE 35
Over-winter kill of old matted sward with paraquat; note rotted mat.

ICI Plant Protection Division

the stubble weed problem. On the other hand increases in labour, machinery and fuel costs inevitably mean that a system employing more of any or all of these inputs (as traditional ploughing and cultivations do) must become more expensive annually relative to a more streamlined technique. As an example, cost comparisons in 1978 showed a £7 per hectare difference, whereas for 1979 it was (as shown above) £11 per hectare. In 1980, it would have been likely to increase still further, though of course the herbicide bill, which forms a larger proportion of the direct drilling costs than is the case with ploughing, would also have risen.

The farms on which direct drilling can make the greatest contribution towards cost saving are those on which the major enterprise is cereal growing. Theophilus surveyed a number of farms where the area of cereals grown was in the region of 150–180 hectares and on these farms considerable savings in machinery fixed costs were considered feasible; in fact, almost the total savings of fixed costs by direct drilling instead of ploughing (£16 out of £17 per ha) were in respect of machinery.

An examination of comparative costs for spraying materials and for fuel and oil shows very marked savings in fuel (Table 32).

Table 32. Variable costs (£ per hectare)

Item	Direct drilling	Reduced cultivations	Ploughing
Spray materials	13.00	6.50	3.25
Fuel, etc.	3.56	15.35	21.85

(Source: after Theophilus, ADAS, Cambridge 1979) (Ref. 5)

On farms where there are other major enterprises in addition to cereals, such as potatoes and sugar beet, the labour force, amount of cultivating equipment (including ploughs) and number and size of tractors are governed by the requirements of such crops. So on these farms it is likely that fixed costs will not be reduced even if the cereals are all direct drilled. The potential advantages of direct drilling in terms of increased productivity are considerable, however, and will apply under all farming systems *where cereals are an important sector*. This is considered in detail below.

On farms where the aim is to grow a large area of cereals, the greater potential profitability of winter cereals sets the objective, i.e. to drill as much winter wheat and barley as soil, climate and other farm enterprises will permit. The major constraints which tend to limit the amount of winter cereals are soil type, autumn weather, date of harvest and competing demands for available labour—the autumn 'peak'.

Where root crops and cereals are grown, labour following harvest is required for straw disposal, stubble cleaning, ploughing for winter cereals and for lifting potatoes and/or roots. After a late harvest these operations may well coincide, and often the cereal crop suffers, some of it going in late, in deteriorating weather and soil conditions. At worst, a proportion of the area earmarked for winter wheat may finish up carrying spring barley (see Table 33).

Table 33. Comparative gross margins of winter wheat and spring barley

| Winter wheat | | Spring barley | |
Item	£/ha	Item	£/ha
Income/ha (based on 4.65t/ha @ £90 per tonne	418.5	Income/ha (based on 3.97t/ha @ £85 per tonne	337.45
Less Variable costs		Less Variable costs	
Seed £36		Seed £30	
Fertiliser £34		Fertiliser £33	
Spray £30	100.0	Spray £16	79.00
GM/ha	£318.5	GM/ha	£258.45

(Source: after Theophilus, ADAS, Cambridge, 1979) (Ref. 5)

It follows that on soils and in situations where direct drilling is a practical proposition the system has much to offer by giving the farmer more *time*. The process of ploughing, breaking up the furrow-slice and producing a suitable seedbed takes time even in favourable weather conditions. It is interesting to note that the area of winter wheat grown in England and Wales in 'wetter than normal' and 'good' autumns since 1965 reflects the problem. Good autumn weather 1971, '72, '73, '74, '78—higher areas of winter wheat; wet autumn weather 1966, '69, '76, '77—lower areas of winter wheat.

It has been estimated that direct drilling increases the area of crop that can be drilled in a given time between five- and six-fold (see Table 34).

Detailed studies of comparative energy requirements, labour requirements, running costs and area capability of different cultivation treatments were made in long-term experiments by NIAE scientists at three sites between 1971 and 1977. The sites were at Boxworth on calcareous clay loam (winter wheat), Rothamsted on silty clay loam (winter wheat) and NIAE HQ at Silsoe, again on a silty clay loam (spring barley).[4] The term 'area capability' defines

Table 34. Work rates

	Ploughing	Direct drilling
Man hours per hectare	5·2	1·0
Hectares established in a 40-hour week	7·2	40·0

(Source: after Theophilus, ADAS, Cambridge, 1979) (Ref. 5)

the area of cereal that could be planted by a particular cultivation system in the time available in the autumn (and spring) assuming all other factors to be favourable. The averages for the six years of the experiment at Boxworth and Rothamsted (both winter wheat experiments on heavy land) are shown in Table 35 below.

A study of the results will indicate:

1. That, not surprisingly, spraying and direct drilling was *markedly* the most economical of the 'cultivation' systems in terms of energy requirement.
2. Direct drilling on all sites was most economical in labour requirement.
3. Direct drilling at Boxworth and at Rothamsted was very decidedly the front-runner in terms of 'area' capability.
4. From the viewpoint of costs per hectare (which are displayed in Table 35 in terms of *1979* costs), spraying and direct drilling was markedly ·cheaper than ploughing or chisel ploughing, and about in line with the shallow plough and the rotary digger at Boxworth. At Rothamsted, however, costs of mouldboard ploughing, chisel ploughing and direct drilling were of the same order, with shallow ploughing and the rotary digger proving lower.

Patterson and his colleagues also compared fuel consumption involved in all their experimental cultivation treatments and found direct drilling to be far and away the most economical. Taking fuel consumption by ploughing as 100, figures for chisel ploughing (followed by harrowing and drilling) and for direct drilling were 96 and 15 respectively.

In summarising this six-year experiment the workers concluded that direct drilling offered a number of economic advantages (as described above); its limitations were concerned mainly with the poorer performance of the direct drill (a 15-row triple-disc machine) in wet conditions, especially on heavy soil with spring

Table 35. Labour requirements, costs, energy requirements and area capability for cultivation systems

Cultivation system	No. of years	Crop and site*	Depth of primary cultivation mm	Labour requirement man hr/ha	Net energy mJ/ha†	Cost‡ £/ha	Area capability ha
Plough, cultivator, drill	6 6	1 2	220 220	4·0 2·6	320 180	46.60 27.50	88 132
Chisel plough (2 passes), cultivator, drill	6** 6**	1 2	130 145	3·3 2·4	286 194	37.60 22.90	107 142
Shallow plough, combined cultivator/drill	6 6	1 2	110 105	2·0 1·6	187 108	23.20 18.00	178 214
Rotary digger, combined cultivator/drill	4 4	1 2	100/200 100/200	1·8 1·4	176 144	23.60 18.40	197 235
Sprayer, direct drill	5 4	1 2	N.A. N.A.	1·0 0·9	38 43	25.00 24.20	353 368

N.A. = not applicable
* 1 = Boxworth, winter wheat
  2 = Rothamsted, winter wheat
** In 1976–7 only one pass of chisel plough required
† Energy at the implement connection
‡ Based on costs in 1979
(Source: Patterson, Chamen & Richardson, National Institute of Agricultural Engineering, Silsoe)

barley, on uneven stubble surfaces, in the presence of loose cereal stubble and chopped straw, and under hard and dry conditions where tilth was lacking.

FARM MANAGEMENT IMPLICATIONS

It is suggested that before embarking upon extensive direct drilling, certainly before purchasing a direct drill, the implications and potential advantages of adopting the technique be studied on a whole-farm basis.

Consider the following examples:

Example 1
Mr Brian Finney, Regional Machinery Adviser, ADAS Eastern Region, Cambridge and his colleagues looked at the possibility of direct drilling as part of a farm system on a farm on clay soil near Cambridge. Direct drilling and conventional cultivations were compared experimentally for the three years 1974–6[2].

There are 172 ha under cultivation on the farm. Table 36 shows comparative average yields of winter wheat under the cultivation systems compared, together with valuations of the crops produced.

Table 36. Comparison of winter wheat yields from different cultivation treatments (3-year averages), Grange Farm, Knapwell, Cambs 1974–6

Method of cultivation	Yield (tonne/ha)	Estimated total tonnage (tonne)	Value @ £78·15 per tonne (corrected for small-plot yields)
Tine cultivation (farm system)	5·01	830·0	£67,450
Experimental			
Plough	5·60	929·2	£67,458
Reduced cultivation	5·15	853·5	£61,959
Direct drill	5·61	931·4	£67,610

(After: Finney, ADAS, E. Region) (Ref. 2)

In 1976, 205 litres of paraquat were used in conjunction with the farmer's tine cultivation system. It was estimated that a change to a full direct drilling system would increase the requirement of paraquat to 423 litres.

The farm labour force consisted of the farmer and two men. There were two crawler tractors (one fitted with a chisel plough), three 2-wheel drive tractors, two other tractors (one fitted with a

fork-lift and the other with a sprayer), also a mouldboard plough.
Four possible systems were explored:

1. To use the mouldboard plough as the basis, with existing labour
   and machinery. On that soil it was estimated that spring barley
   would have to substitute for winter wheat on 47 hectares, at a
   cost (i.e. a 'penalty') computed at £133 per ha.
2. To equip and sow a full winter wheat crop based on the mouldboard system. This would require an extra man with a large
   tractor and plough, necessitating an increased cost of £5,700.
3. To aim at a 'reduced cultivation' system. On the three-year
   average shown in Table 36 the 'penalty' would be £5,500.
4. To direct drill the entire farm, a practical proposition from the
   agronomic viewpoint. Even if the farmer dispensed with only
   one crawler tractor and purchased a drill at a cost of £6,400
   (1976 price) amortised over ten years, that would mean an extra
   annual cost of £640. Adding the cost of increased herbicide (i.e.
   218 litres *extra* of paraquat) and bearing in mind a three-year
   average yield, Finney estimated that savings in costs would
   balance out. It seemed from this exercise that working towards
   direct drilling on a farm system was the most realistic approach
   and, indeed, this was the choice made by the farmer.

Example 2

The computer makes it possible to compare and contrast a series of
systems, based on certain assumptions, and in many aspects of agriculture very considerable use is made of computer facilities to
enable farmers to study the possible effects of changing the balance
of their farming by increasing this enterprise, discarding that,
diversifying, and so on. In 1977 ICI[1] used their Billingham computer to study the likely impact on three farm 'models' (an arable
farm, a mixed arable/stock farm, and a dairy farm) of using direct
drilling wherever practical. The three farms do exist, and their
owners provided ICI with the information required for the computer exercise. The details below are for the mixed arable/stock farm.

The calculations made by the computer were based on 'known'
factors: suitability of soil for direct drilling; time taken to drill one
hectare of a particular crop by direct drilling, and by traditional
systems in current use on the farm; availability of time on the land;
and other 'conserving' factors already mentioned in this chapter.
Parity of yield by direct drilling was also considered a fair assumption on the soils in question. Finally, the calculations assumed the
need to purchase a direct drill and that the direct drill would be

used also for conventional drilling.

The meat of the computer exercise is displayed in Table 37; the financial summaries before and after the exercise are shown in Table 38, and the capital requirements if the farm were to adopt drilling are outlined in Table 39.

Table 37. Computer exercise on a mixed arable/stock farm

Crop	Original Programme (ha)	Direct drilling programme (ha)
Oilseed rape	40	43
Winter wheat	60	85
Winter barley	40	62
Spring barley	70	66
Permanent pasture	20	20 (improved)
Temporary grass	76	43 (direct drilled into stubble)
Root crops		
Maincrop turnips traditionally sown	12	
Stubble turnip direct drilled into stubble		19
Swede—direct drilled		4
	(number)	*(number)*
Livestock		
Ewe flock	300	300
Store lambs for fattening	300	300
Suckler cows	40	50

(Source: After Arnold & Page, ICI 1977)

Table 38. Financial summaries

	Original programme		Programme with direct drilling	
	£ total	£/ha	£ total	£/ha
Farm gross margin	68,431	215	77,612	245
Total fixed costs	41,328	131	42,667	133
Management and investment income	£27,103	£84	£34,945	£111

(Source: after Arnold and Page, ICI 1977)

In 1981, of course, the figure in Table 39 would be higher. On the other hand, returns per hectare of wheat, barley and oilseed rape

Table 39. Mixed arable/stock farm—capital requirements if farm adopted direct drilling as a system

Item	Cost (£)
Direct drill (£3000 less sale of old drill and cultivating equipment at £1000 net)	2,000
Grain storage—150 tonne at £25 per tonne	3,750
10 suckler cows at £300 per head	3,000
	£8,750
	N.B. at 1977 value

(Source: after Arnold & Page, ICI, 1977)

would also be higher, thus inflating the figures shown under 'gross margin' in the financial summaries in Table 38.

The computer exercise showed that a direct drill (purchased) and some cultivating equipment (existing) would enable the new system (Table 37) to operate with an unchanged labour force, giving an increased Management and Investment Income of £7,842. To be fair, the computer exercise showed also that an increase of £4,828 could come from a farm reorganisation within the limits of the current resources of the farm without any capital investment or the purchase of a direct drill. Thus the *net* increase resulting from the adoption of direct drilling is computed at £7,842 − £4,828 = £3,014, showing a return on the capital investment (£8,750, see Table 39) of 34%.

The major contributions to the increased income would be:

1. Increase in the area grown (an extra 47 hectares) of the more profitable cereals—winter wheat and barley.
2. Improvement of stock-carrying levels by direct drilling new grass into stubble and improving permanent grass, coupled with:
3. An increase in average nitrogen levels (not practical with *under-sown* cereals) thus enabling more intensive stocking, and releasing land for more cash crops, especially winter cereals.
4. Increase in forage crops (catch crops and swedes) by direct drilling.

A computer exercise such as that described above does not tell all the story, though it is possible to build in 'hazards' and adduce from knowledge and experience what differential effects such hazards might have on different cultivation systems. It seems a very sensible approach, however. The result of the exercise may not be a cast-iron guarantee, but neither would a prediction of the likely out-turn from a well-tried traditional approach. Such an exercise would provide a useful guide, but before it is even started a farmer should, with whatever help and advice he feels he needs, study the agronomic suitability of his farm for 'no-plough' cultivating and direct drilling techniques. More will be said about this later (see also Chapter 4).

It has already been conceded that the figures shown in the various tables included in this chapter are somewhat outdated, but the relative costs of the different systems under review have not altered to any great degree and are still valid. A farmer doing his own calculations would naturally use up-to-date figures.

To justify the purchase of a direct drill on a mixed arable/stock farm, a farmer should be growing a substantial area of cereals, and in the ICI computer exercise, and the ADAS East Anglian study described above, the areas of cereals (over 100 and 165 ha respectively) were certainly large enough to justify such a purchase.

ADAS[3] suggest that more than 90 ha of cereals would have to be grown to make drill purchase a better economic proposition than employing a contractor. Much depends upon the machine itself and upon future developments, but there is no doubt that a specialist direct drill like the MF 130 or the Bettinson fit into the large cereal enterprise. On the other hand, the farmer with these machines may also use them for conventional drilling where soil conditions are suitable, and this could justify their choice as *the* farm drill. Put another way, the farmer wishing to direct drill a large cereal area plus, say, oilseed rape, *must* purchase his own drill whereas the farmer with fewer hectares has a choice between purchase and employing a contractor.

ADAS conclude that 'generally speaking the introduction of direct drilling on a mixed arable farm system remains a doubtful proposition if the direct costs of the direct drilling and alternative cultivation system are considered. The crucial element is the size of the cereal enterprise'.[3] A glance back at Table 37, however, indicates that on a large mixed arable/stock farm there can be substantial advantage in productivity from adopting rapid cultivation techniques with existing equipment and labour.

REFERENCES

1. ARNOLD, R. and PAGE, J. N. (1977), ICI Press Conference, London 1977; also reported in *Proc. Int. Conf. on Energy Conserv.* in *Crop*

Prodn (Massey Univ. N.Z.), 1977, 134–5.

2. FINNEY, J. B. (1976), MAFF, ADAS E Region, *Cereals Cultivation Conf.*, Cambridge, 1976.
3. MAFF, ADAS (1978), *Cereals Without Ploughing*, Profitable Farm Enterprises Booklet 6, MAFF.
4. PATTERSON, D. E., CHAMEN, W. C. T. and RICHARDSON, C. D. (1980), *NIAE J Ag. Engng. Res* (1980), **25**, 1–35.
5. THEOPHILUS, T. W. D. (1979), *Progress with Cultivations*, NAC Conf., Stoneleigh, 6 March 1979.

Chapter 8
PRACTICAL GUIDELINES— CEREALS AND OILSEED RAPE

1. CEREALS

In the foregoing chapters the influence of direct drilling and reduced cultivation systems on a wide range of factors has been discussed in some detail. During the twenty years since these alternative systems received serious attention, a great deal has been learned. Much information is now available for the farmer contemplating 'no-plough' techniques for cereals, but the result in the end depends on the skill with which he manages his soil and crop. This is probably even more important than with traditional husbandry because, in direct drilling in particular, the farmer has to 'get it right' first time.

BASIC QUESTIONS

The first question which the farmer must ask himself is—will it profit me *to consider* direct drilling my cereal crops? Remember the discussions on the economics of direct drilling and the examples given in Chapter 7. The farmer who grows a substantial area of winter cereals, even if he grows *only* cereals, is always under heavy pressure in the autumn. If he grows a root crop as well, this pressure is greatly increased. He has a heavy harvesting task which may be delayed by bad weather, and this decreases the time available to him for drilling his next winter crop. It is undeniable that late autumn drilling of cereals imposes a yield penalty, and in really bad autumns the winter cereal target may not be achieved. Even if the target *is* achieved in spite of poor autumn weather, it may have been done by 'smudging' in some of the later drilled winter corn, especially on the stickier soils. The main agronomic motivator in this instance is the reduction of time spent on the land in deteriorating weather; the more streamlined technique also cuts down the heavy traffic associated with ploughing and subsequent cultivations. Taking all these points into consideration, the answer to the question would therefore be 'yes'.

This answer, however, depends also on his being able to answer the second basic question: 'Have I, on my farm, a substantial area of soil suitable for direct drilling?' To this end the farmer must be able to identify his own soil types and to check them with the list of categorised soils shown in Tables 27, 28 and 29 in Chapter 4. He can get help from ADAS soil scientists and others, but it is likely that the majority of cereal growers are well able to classify their own soils. Basically, as has already been experienced, the soils most suitable for direct drilling are those which are well-drained and resistant to compaction—chalk and limestone soils, well-drained loamy soils, peaty soils, peats, soils with reasonably high organic matter content, and self-mulching, well-structured clays. Good vertical communication through pores and fissures is also of great importance. These soil types are all defined as Category 1 (see Chapter 4). If the soils are in Category 2, mainly because they are inadequately drained, then it may be possible, by installing efficient field drainage, to up-grade to Category 1 status.

Assuming that the basic questions of economics and soil suitability can be answered favourably, and either direct drilling or some form of reduced cultivation system is envisaged, the next step is to plan ahead, that is, to 'farm towards' the alternative method, and this means thinking ahead at least one year, preferably longer.

PLANNING A CHANGEOVER

For the farmer who grows a substantial area of cereal plus cash roots such as potatoes and sugar beet, it is very likely that the autumn 'peak' is the factor which is motivating him to consider a change. Obviously, if he is aiming to grow an increased area of winter cereals, he will need to calculate how much extra grain storage space he will need, unless he is planning a straight switch between winter and spring cereals. The mixed arable/stock farmer will have to do a paper excercise similar to those quoted in Chapter 7 in order to see how he will need to alter the balance of his arable and forage crops, and what he will achieve thereby.

REMEDY DRAINAGE DEFICIENCIES

Drainage may be improved by putting in a complete pipe-drain network, but the exact nature of the system required is of course determined by soil and situation. On deep peats, for example, providing the drainage ditches are kept open, pipe drains may not be necessary. Where soil permeability is only moderate, pipe drains placed 20–60 metres apart and as deep as the drainage ditches will permit will probably do the job without any permeable fill. On heavier clay, however, permeability is likely to be too slow to provide efficient natural drainage, especially in winter; so pipe drains must be supplemented by moling (or deep subsoiling) with permeable back-fill over the pipes to 'link' the supplementary system with them.[1]

Mole Drainage
Mole ploughs produce channels 50 mm in diameter at a depth of 500–700 mm and if moling is carried out when the subsoil is moist enough to form a channel (but not *too* wet) and the soil above the mole is sufficiently dry, a good channel will be drawn and the soil above the mole will be fissured. May–June, when the soil is drying out, is a good time for moling.

Subsoiling
The main purpose of subsoiling is to lift and shatter compact subsoil, thus the subsoil should be drier than is required for moling. Subsoiling should be carried out only as a supplement to a good pipe drainage system with permeable backfill in order to carry away the water which will move more rapidly through the lower subsoil layers after subsoiling, otherwise waterlogging may ensue.

Soil Loosening at Depth
The 'Paraplow' and the Flat 'A' blade, already mentioned, can be used to loosen the lower soil while retaining the firm level seedbed which is ideal for direct drilling.

SUPPRESS PERENNIAL WEEDS IN ADVANCE

Next, the weed flora on the fields (arable or grass) involved in the new system should be studied; in particular, perennials, especially creeping grass weeds like couch and creeping bent or water-grass must be suppressed before going into a direct drilling or shallow cultivation regime. These grasses will compound the adverse effects of direct drilling into compacted, ill-drained and/or water-logged soil, but they will threaten even a well-drilled crop if they are left unchecked (see also Chapter 5).

If the field is in cereals, then heavy infestations of couch should be tackled *a year before* direct drilling is contemplated. Likewise, if the field is in grass, perennial weeds such as docks should be tackled a year ahead. It is feasible to direct drill, however, where *light to moderate* infestations of perennials, grass or broadleaves, have been treated with the appropriate herbicide *in the same year*; this is especially the case where glyphosate has been applied *before* harvesting the previous crop (see later).

CEREALS INTO STUBBLE

Removal of Straw and Trash

The clear benefits of burning straw prior to direct drilling have already been described in Chapter 3. The yield advantage to the subsequent crop (especially if direct drilled, but independent of cultivation system employed), added to the cost of cultivation necessary to achieve satisfactory disposal of straw without burning, makes this practice a very desirable preparatory operation. Provided the burning is carried out responsibly, having regard to the NFU Code of Practice, risks can be reduced very significantly. There are variants of the system advocated by the NFU; in general terms the major elements of the operation should include the following:

1. Notify the Fire Service well in advance of the intended 'burn'.
2. Produce a cultivated 'fire-break' free of vegetation, around the field headland, say about 4 metres wide. Before using the cultivator (or the plough) to achieve this, move any loose straw on this strip well into the field.
3. First light the field on the down-wind side, and back-burn at least 30 metres before attempting to light up-wind.
4. Have a member of the farm staff in charge of the operation equipped (ideally) with a suitable vehicle towing a water bowser, and with a forestry-type beater, so that should the 'burn' cross the fire-break, he is able to deal with it. The man in charge should stay in the field all the time that the fire is burning.

If there is a cover of green weed between the swathes of loose straw, desiccation with a low rate of paraquat (1 litre product per hectare) will assist the 'burn'.

Deal with Weeds in Stubbles

The major herbicides which are basic to the practice of direct drilling are paraquat and glyphosate. These are both widely known—a brief description of the properties of each is given below. N.B. For the sake of clarity rates of application are expressed in litres per hectare of the commercial products.

Paraquat ('Gramoxone'), discovered by ICI in the late 1950s, is sold as the dichloride, formulated with a wetting agent. It will kill all green aerial growth with which it makes contact, and it is almost instantaneously inactivated by adsorption on all mineral soils containing a reasonable clay fraction, and on soils rich in organic matter. On such soils it is perfectly feasible to drill the new seeds immediately after spraying, or even before spraying the old stubble or sward; on lighter, sandy soils with fewer, more widely dispersed clay particles, a period of three days is counselled between spraying and expected date of emergence of a sown crop, as the paraquat ion takes just a little longer to reach the more scattered adsorption sites.

Paraquat is rain-fast, so rain falling as soon as ten minutes after the application of paraquat will not lessen the effectiveness of the herbicide, as it is absorbed into plant leaves and stems extremely rapidly. If applied late in the day towards dusk, paraquat will move further through the sprayed plant before destroying the plant tissue; thus it may work a little more slowly, but rather more effectively, than when sprayed in bright sunlight. This herbicide is at its best on annuals (grasses and broadleaved) and on tufted perennial grasses, though it is effective in suppressing creeping bent when applied in the autumn. It will kill couch grass shoots, but the weed will recover from a single application. Applied in small doses (0·7 1/ha) each time regrowth reaches about 5 cm, it will eventually kill the weed.

Glyphosate ('Round-up'), discovered and developed by Monsanto, is a phosphonate derivative of glycine. Like paraquat, glyphosate is inactivated on contact with the soil, though the mechanism of inactivation is different. It is active against a range of annual and perennial weeds. It is absorbed through the foliage and translocated efficiently within plants, through the aerial growth and into rhizomes, stolons, and root systems. Unlike paraquat, glyphosate acts slowly, and it also requires *at least* six hours without rain following its application for fully effective action. There is no doubt that for controlling couch grass in particular, also for suppressing deep-rooted perennial weeds such as docks (*Rumex* spp) in the absence of a crop, glyphosate is more effective than paraquat. On the other hand, the slower rate of kill, and the need for substanial aerial growth as a 'target', coupled with the need for a dry period after spraying, makes glyphosate in these respects a less flexible tool than paraquat for autumn use, especially in a wet autumn, when time and fine periods are at a premium.

In many respects paraquat and glyphosate are complementary, though in commercial terms they are, of course, in competition.

For couch control the application of glyphosate to the weed in a cereal crop before harvest is recommended by the manufacturers. This makes good sense because couch growth burgeons as the cereal crop ripens and light enters the crop—it thus presents a better target for the herbicide.

Rates of Application for Suppression of Stubble Weeds

Paraquat
Much depends on the nature of the weed to be destroyed. ICI recommend 5·5 1/ha for crops direct drilled into stubble and 5·5–8·5 1/ha for crops direct drilled into grass. If the weeds are mainly annuals 3 1/ha is usually adequate. The weed should have sufficient green growth to provide a target for the spray, and burning should have stimulated a good germination of annual weeds, both grass and broadleave. To improve this 'braird' of weeds a light 'scratching' following burning will be helpful, and will also produce some surface tilth.

Glyphosate
A rate of 1·5 1/ha is considered adequate for the control of seedling weeds, both grass and broadleaved. A higher rate (4 1/ha) is advised for couch grass control and for suppressing perennial weeds along the lines already discussed (see Chapter 5).

Delayed Weed Germination
One aspect of weed suppression that must be considered and well planned concerns 'volunteer' cereals, wild oats and blackgrass. Winter cereals repay direct drilling as early as is feasible in the autumn, winter barley in late September, and winter wheat before mid-October, so it is quite possible that these annual grasses and 'volunteers' may not oblige by germinating as a 'flush' before drilling. Burning will help, but a late harvest will lead to delayed brairding. Moreover, if there should be a fair proportion of organic matter in the surface of the soil, this may reduce somewhat the effectiveness of certain pre-emergence grass weedkillers (see Chapter 5). All of this may be dealt with by planning a programme around early post-emergence weedkillers.

Condition of Soil Surface

Where the soil surface has been rutted or compacted during harvest it is essential to prepare the ground before drilling with a light cultivation. DO NOT direct drill unless the surface conditions are right.

CEREALS INTO GRASS

There are three agronomic advantages in direct drilling cereals into grass. First, the soil structure beneath the sward is ideal for the start of a run of cereals; second, direct drilling preserves that structure, and third, stones and wild oats seeds remain buried.

Provided couch grass is not a serious weed, and provided that deep-rooted perennial broadleaved weeds have been dealt with, the sward may be destroyed by paraquat; if these perennials are dominant in the sward glyphosate is likely to be a better choice.

1. Into Leys

● *Winter cereals*

Apply paraquat at 4–5·5 l/ha, followed 7–10 days later by 1·5–3 l/ha using the higher rate where timothy, cocksfoot or tall fescue are present, and the lower rate if only meadow-grasses and ryegrass are present.

Alternatively apply glyphosate at 3–5 l/ha in early July/mid-August.

● *Spring cereals*

Apply paraquat at 4–5·5 l/ha in November/December, and in spring apply 1·5–3 l/ha.

Glyphosate should be applied as recommended for winter cereals.

2. Into Old Matted Grassland

To direct drill into old grass takes time, and a winter cereal is not a suitable crop for this purpose. The best approach is to spray the old sward in the autumn with 4–5·5 l/ha of paraquat or 6 l/ha of glyphosate and allow the winter to assist in breaking up the dead 'mat'.

Spray any regrowth with 1·5–3 l/ha of paraquat in spring and direct drill spring cereals.

CHOICE OF DRILL

Machinery available for direct drilling has been described in detail in Chapter 6. For cereals, the basic choice lies between the big triple-disc drills and the cultivator drills. Remember that if the soil is wet but not compacted direct drilling may be feasible, but, under these conditions, triple-disc coulters may tend to leave smeared slots. Whatever drill is employed, it is essential to ensure that the slots are closed and 'tilthy'. If necessary, harrow, and if soil conditions permit or dictate, roll after drilling.

SEED RATE

There is no need to sow extra seed when direct drilling (see Chapter 2), and the choice between combine-drilling or drilling seed and broadcasting fertiliser is governed by the same 'rules' as for conventional drilling.

FERTILISERS

Phosphate and Potash
It has already been stated that uptake of P and K is not affected by direct drilling, and that surface-applied nutrients, though tending to remain in the surface few centimetres, will be taken up and utilised just as efficiently as nutrients incorporated in the topsoil to plough depth.

Nitrogen
Concerning N there are differing views. Some people believe direct drilled crops need extra nitrogen. In the author's experience some nitrogen in the seedbed on direct drilled winter cereals can be helpful, but there seems no need to assume that the *total* nitrogen should be increased *because* the crop is being direct drilled.

Lime
Experience has shown that with continuous direct drilling over a period the pH in the surface 2–3 cm of soil can drop *seriously* over a period of years. Surface pH should therefore be checked and lime applied if necessary, or at least a fertiliser containing lime. These points will be illustrated in the case studies later in the chapter.

PESTS

Be on the lookout for slugs. Where burning has not been attempted or where it has not been effective, the trash may harbour this pest. If necessary apply a molluscicide in bran or in pellet form. Metaldehyde and methiocarb are the two commonly used materials.

Frit fly (as already mentioned in Chapter 5) can be a threat to winter wheat direct drilled into chemically-killed pasture or leys. It appears that winter barley is less subject to frit attack. The larvae from the third generation of frit fly in the autumn remain in the surface and feed on the newly emerging cereal seedlings, eating the centre tiller of the young plants. Frit numbers may be as high as 50,000,000 per hectare in some years! Early advice on this problem was to leave as long an interval as practicable between killing the sward and drilling winter cereal; it appears, however, that frit fly larvae can exist in the killed sward for many weeks, so leaving an interval is no guarantee that the frit larvae will starve!

In experiments by ADAS, ICI Plant Protection, and others, numerous insecticides have been tested. Recently, best results have been achieved with the Fisons product 'Garvox' which contains bendiocarb (see Chapter 9).

General experience has been that the control of frit fly by insecticides in direct drilled cereals has been rather more rewarding than in direct drilled grass. That being said, there is room for much improvement in both consistency and effectiveness of control measures against this pest

CEREAL CASE STUDIES

The pros and cons of direct drilling and 'non-ploughing' cultivation systems for cereals may be best displayed by looking at a number of instances in which these systems have been tested or utilised commercially, on a farm scale and over a long period. Case studies are presented concerning five farming enterprises.

1. Drayton EHF—reduced cultivations since the late 1960s.
2. Mr R H Jenkinson—direct drilling on brash and calcareous clay.
3. Mr R Holbrook—direct drilling on boulder clay in the East of England.
4. Mr M Bendall—cereals and grass, direct drilled into Cotswold brash and and alluvial soils.
5. High Mowthorpe EHF—who have had problems with direct drilling.

Drayton Experimental Husbandry Farm, near Stratford on Avon, Warwickshire[3]

Drayton, once the Grassland Research Station, covers 182 hectares of heavy Lias clay, mostly of the Evesham series (calcareous). Winter crops outyield spring crops by a decisive margin, and the most profitable cereal is winter wheat. For this reason they follow an intensive cereal rotation over a nine-year period, containing seven winter crops of which five are wheat. The keynote of such a rotation is a very high autumn workload, which led to an investigation of simplified methods of producing seedbeds. It must be emphasised that Drayton has four important advantages.

- The soil is well structured;
- Drainage is adequate;
- There are very few perennial grass weeds,
- They are not troubled with disease problems to any degree.

The major bottleneck on heavy land, especially under such an autumn-biassed rotation, is ploughing, and even after heavy capital expenditure on large tractors and machinery, ploughing is a slow process, and produces large clods which in turn require time and much work to convert into a reasonable seedbed. Heavy cultivators and chisel-ploughs were tested out at Drayton and certainly speeded up the work, but they still produced clods and consumed a great deal of power.

After further investigation Drayton have settled on the use of lighter-tined cultivators, starting shallow and going deeper, pass by pass, to a limit of 10 cm. This work can be accomplished with smaller tractors and produces reasonably small clods. Plates 32–4 show:

- clods produced on Drayton soil by ploughing;
- cloddy tilth produced by two discings of the ploughed soil;
- a much improved tilth produced by two passes of a spring-tined cultivator *without* ploughing.

The spring-tined cultivator used at Drayton is the 'Flexitine', 3½ metres wide with fourteen tines arranged on three beams to minimise blocking. Table 40 shows crop yields following (a) ploughing and discing, (b) chisel-ploughing and (c) cultivation by Flexitine, over five seasons from 1972 to 1976 inclusive.

Drayton would have been content had they achieved parity of yields, using this simplified cultivation system—in fact, over the five-year period, they achieved slightly better yields!

The Lower Lias clay (Evesham series) has 50–60% clay fraction in the top 20 cm, which confers upon it a stable structure; moreover it shrinks and cracks. It weathers well (is self-mulching) and does not 'cap'. It is rather heavy to work but the Drayton cultivation system makes the best of the soil and maintains the organic matter level. The tile drainage system needs to be supplemented and subsoiling is carried out once in each nine-year arable rotation.

Couch grass is sparse and the 'Flexitine' no doubt keeps what

PLATE 32
Clods produced by ploughing.
Drayton EHF Crown Copyright

PLATE 33
Tilth produced by disc-ings after ploughing.
Drayton EHF Crown Copyright

PLATE 34
Tilth produced by two passes of a spring-tine cultivator *without* ploughing.
Drayton EHF Crown Copyright

Table 40. Crop yields at Drayton EHF (tonne/ha)

Year	Crop	Plough	Chisel plough	Flexitine
1972	Winter wheat	5·30		5·42
1973	Winter wheat	3·86	4·53	4·52
1974	Winter beans	5·25	5·32	5·33
1975	Winter wheat	4·09	4·25	3·90
1976	Winter wheat	3·42	4·06	3·55
	Average 7 (plough = 100)	100	103	103

(Source: Oliphant, Drayton EHF 1978) (Ref. 3) Crown Copyright

there is in check; there are annual grass weeds, including wild oats, most of the latter fortunately autumn-germinating. Straw is dealt with either by:

● burning—following the NFU Code with their own variation; or
● baling and carting off, and burning the remaining stubble; or
● baling and carting off and working-in the remaining stubble—this is done closely behind the combine.

Cultivations start as soon as possible after straw removal, and field by field in the order in which drilling will be done. The 'Flexi-tine' makes two passes (three if the stubble has not been burnt) provided weather conditions are suitable. If conditions are wet, one pass is made; if conditions improve, further passes will be made, but if wet conditions persist, any emerging weeds are killed with paraquat (at 1·4 litres in 225 litres water per ha) pre-drilling.

The above system is followed for winter seedbeds out of stubble; there are two other cropping situations:

1. Winter wheat seedbeds out of grassland
First the grass is grazed bare, then the ground is subsoiled or mole-drained in July, and finally the land is cultivated in late July/early August.

Tight grazing is essential to prevent blocking the cultivators with trash, though the rotary digger which is now used will probably render this point less important. Although the sward is not normally sprayed, paraquat may be used if weather conditions cause delay, or keep the sward green in the clod. July is a good time for subsoiling because the soil is usually dry enough to shatter.

Drayton like the rotary digger and claim that it is faster and breaks up the sod without bringing up raw material from below; moreover, it can be pulled by a two-wheeled tractor. The farm staff are sure that the extra weathering time between initial cultivations and final seedbed preparation (two months) may be contributing to increases in wheat yields following grass, as compared with ploughing.

2. Spring barley seedbeds out of stubble

The Drayton approach involves two passes in the autumn with the 'Flexitine' after disposing of straw. In the spring, as early as possible, weed growth is sprayed with paraquat at 2 litres product/ha and barley is sown with a disc drill and harrowed in. Winter weathering plays a big part in producing a suitable seedbed for the barley which is also undersown with grass seed.

The Drayton staff thus follow a 'non-plough' cultivation system. They are looking at direct drilling for their winter corn and, where they do this, they substitute paraquat for their pre-drilling weed control cultivation. The autumn cultivations are still basic to their system, however.

Mr R H Jenkinson, Manor Farm, Eastleach, Gloucestershire[8]

Mr Jenkinson farms 770 hectares, half on Cotswold brash with a fair clay content, and half on Evesham-series calcareous clay. In the late 1960s he and his partner decided upon cereals as the major crop enterprise, and settled for a system involving the bulk of the land (566 ha) in winter corn. 182 ha were left in permanent grass to maintain a flock of sheep and to feed and fatten bought-in steers.

The problem which presented itself was to drill the large area of winter cereals and to harvest it satisfactorily, and Mr Jenkinson joined with Mr John Page of ICI Plant Protection in development trials with direct drilling. Forty hectares of cereals were direct drilled with Rotaseeder in the autumn of 1968. Of this 16 ha failed and only 10 ha could be considered satisfactory! No cereals were direct drilled in 1969 but in 1970 52 ha were direct drilled, this time with the IH 6–2 drill[4].

By this time the *potential* advantages of direct drilling at Eastleach had become clear, and during the early 1970s both Mr Jenkinson and Mr Page learnt a lot about the technique, in particular, the need to direct drill early in the autumn, and to ensure a surface 'mini-tilth' which could only be produced on soil in good physical condition. During this learning period direct drilling machinery was also improving, and the main drill used at this time was the International Harvester IH 6–2 cultivator drill. The cropping was settled at continuous winter barley on the brash and continuous winter wheat on the clay. Direct drilling was introduced gradually;

some fields have been direct drilled every year since 1969 and *all* fields have been direct drilled for at least six years.

Winter barley is favoured because it is easy to manage and yields well; it will grow on the poorer soil and is less sensitive to drought than either winter wheat or spring barley—it is also a good 'smother' crop. Barley is ready to harvest early, thus spreading the workload, giving more time for the drilling operation. In 1979–80 365 hectares of winter barley were direct drilled. In that season 188 hectares of winter wheat were direct drilled, and 12 hectares of spring barley and 7 hectares of spring wheat were grown conventionally.

Mr Jenkinson's approach, step by step, is as follows:

1. Know all about the fields, especially about possible constraints, i.e. drainage inadequacies, pans, rock 'plates' (a feature of some of the Eastleach fields).
2. Clean the headlands.
3. Have soil analyses carried out (both physical and chemical).
4. *Aim* to have the land ready for drilling in the second week in September. Drill the winter barley in the last two weeks of September and the winter wheat in the first half of October, and finish *all* winter cereal drilling by the middle of that month.

Mr Jenkinson estimates that for every week's delay in drilling after the end of October, he pays a penalty of 125 kg of grain per hectare. He has also discovered that, with early drilling, 157 kg/ha of seed is sufficient, whereas for very late drilling he has to sow about 350 kg/ha!

5. *Bale* what straw is needed, leaving a swathe of straw in a circle round the headland, allowing for an adequate (cultivated) firebreak; also leave a few swathes across the field to facilitate burning. With two active men setting fire to the surplus straw around the field, and a third with a Landrover and water-bowser on hand to deal with emergencies, they can burn 120 ha of stubble in a day. The value of a good 'black-burn' for killing weeds is emphasised.
6. After a good burn, a good 'scratch' tilth is produced, no deeper than 2·5 cm. Mr Jenkinson uses an 8-metre Scandinavian C-tine machine, which encourages germination of weed seed. Paraquat is then applied at 2 litres ha to kill the emerged weeds.
7. The cereal seed is now direct drilled, using both the IH 6–2 drill and a Bettinson DD. Choice of drill ('tine' or 'triple disc') depends on soil conditions in each field. The seed is planted at a maximum depth of 2·5 cm, i.e. into the 'scratch-tilth'. Deeper

drilling has been found to cause breaking of the 'below-ground' stems of the seedlings.

8. *Crop protection inputs.* The aim is to remove, in the *autumn,* as many weeds as possible, using appropriate selective broad-leaved and grass weedkillers. Mr Jenkinson's view is that in a thick crop in the spring it is often difficult for applied weedkillers to reach their targets. He has had some success against sterile brome grass. He sprays the areas between the crop headlands and field boundaries with atrazine and the headlands themselves before crop emergence in the autumn with cyanazine ('Fortrol') and follows this up in the spring, where necessary, with metoxuron ('Dosaflo').[4] Appropriate and timely measures are also employed to combat diseases (eyespot, *Rhynchosporium,* mildew and *Septoria,* and rust if it occurs) and all the cereals receive a straw shortener in the spring.

9. *Fertilisers—nitrogen.* Mr Jenkinson believes in adequate nitrogen. The straw-shortener enables him to apply high levels. Both winter cereals receive some seedbed nitrogen. Top dressing for winter wheat is split 50 per cent in late March and 50 per cent in late April (total nitrogen 130–150 kg/ha) whereas for winter barley the split is 70 per cent in March and 30 per cent in April (total nitrogen 120 kg/ha).

One of the heaviest fields (calcareous clay) was considered such a poor proposition during the Second World War, that it was exempted from a Ploughing Order! It was last ploughed by Mr Jenkinson in 1969 and has been direct drilled with winter wheat ever since. The field has benefited enormously after a regime of minimal soil disturbance, with earthworm channels, fissures resulting from shrinking and cracking, and old root channels persisting to give excellent vertical communication from top soil right into the heavy clay subsoil. Apart from a very restricted drainage scheme in the centre of this field which cost £200 before grant, the field is neither tile-drained nor mole-drained, nor is it subsoiled. Yields of winter wheat for the years 1977–9 on the field were:

1977—Huntsman . . . 7·5 tonnes/ha
1978—Huntsman . . . 7·5 tonnes/ha
1979—Aquila . . . 8·75 tonnes/ha

and this reflects yields over the wheat generally. From the 560 ha of winter cereals drilled in 1979 autumn, Mr Jenkinson harvested 3,818 tonnes, giving an all-farm average of 6·81 tonnes/ha (2·6 tons/acre). Winter wheat averaged out at 7·57 t/ha (188 ha) and winter barley at 6·37 t/ha (357 ha). With gross margins of £390/ha for both winter cereals in 1979, and lower fixed costs, and with variable costs in the region of £155/ha, Mr Jenkinson is convinced that his crops and his system of drilling are right for him.

Mr Richard Holbrook, Northey Farm, Bozeat, Northants[7]

The whole of this farm, on the borders of Bucks, Beds, and Northants, lies on chalky boulder clay of the Hanslope Series. Mr Holbrook came to the farm in 1958, and over the years has extended its area to 164 hectares. For as long as people can remember, the farm has been in cereal cropping. The only interruptions to this were a short period during the last war, when part of the farm was used as a bombing range, and some three years during the mid-sixties when Mr Holbrook grew 8 hectares of blackcurrants. Prior to 1968 the cereals grown had been continuous barley, but in that year winter wheat was introduced. The whole farm now is in continuous winter wheat and all bar 12 hectares is grown on contract for breadmaking.

Between 1956 and 1962 Northey Farm was tile-drained with permeable backfill and moled. Despite this investment it was still a major problem to get all the ploughing done and the autumn cereal drilled before the rains came, which quickly brought operations to a standstill. Direct drilling of spring barley was tried first in 1965 on two fields, using paraquat to kill the stubble vegetation. Yields were comparable with ploughing and when winter wheat was introduced in 1968 direct drilling was expanded and no ploughing has taken place at Northey Farm since 1970.

Mr Holbrook ran the farm in the 1960s and early 1970s with one full-time worker plus himself, employing casual labour at harvest. In 1974 he started doing contract drilling for other farmers and in 1980, with two full-time men and occasional help from himself, drilled 1600 hectares for other farmers and in addition sprayed 1600 hectares as contract work. Mr Holbrook owns two Bettinson 4-metre direct drills and is an ICI Plant Protection Approved Contractor.

Because of the urgency to combine 164 hectares, all winter wheat and possibly yielding 7 tonnes per hectare, Mr Holbrook has two combines (3·6 metres and 3 metres) and each combine is fitted with a straw spreader. Following combining, the two rows round the headland are turned inwards. The headlands are then cultivated "clean" with a rotary cultivator, and the field burned. Mr Holbrook prefers burning 'spread straw' rather than swathes. He uses paraquat if the weeds have chitted before drilling, then direct drills the winter wheat during the first fortnight of October with his Bettinson 3D drill. He drills approximately 1–2 cm deep and aims at a seed rate of between 400 and 450 grains per square metre. He broadcasts his autumn fertiliser either before or after drilling and uses 24 kg/ha of P, and 63 kg/ha of N (as ammonium nitrate/lime fertiliser). In the spring, applications of nitrogen are split three times. The first top dressing is applied as early as possible, usually January or February, and is a repeat application of the autumn fertiliser, that is, 24 kg/ha of P and 63 kg/ha of N. The second application normally goes on some time at the end of February or during March and again is 24 kg/ha of P and 63 kg/ha of N. The final application of 95 kg/ha of N is applied at growth stage 30 (Zadok) to growth stage 32. Total fertiliser applied therefore is 72 kg/ha of P and 284 kg/ha of N. No K is applied because the land that Mr Holbrook farms is a montmorillonite clay which contains huge reserves of potassium.

The reason why ammonium nitrate/lime fertiliser is used is that although Hanslope Series clay soil is highly calcareous, continuous direct drilling with minimum soil disturbance means that no lime is brought to the surface and the topsoil could become very acid if high N fertilisers were used. Values of pH are checked every year and those fields which show the top 2·5 cm dropping below 7·0 pH are limed at the rate of 5–6 tonnes/ha.

Couch has been a problem but only in well-defined patches and these were sprayed in June with glyphosate, using a knapsack sprayer. Slug damage has never occurred at Northey Farm. Earthworms have built up considerably under direct drilling and in wet autumns they have disposed of any straw that remained from a poor burn. Wild oats increased massively up to the early 1970s. Since then, annual treatment with difenzoquat has virtually eliminated the problem. Blackgrass is present in some fields. Autumn applications of residual herbicides have proved ineffective, probably due to the high ash content of the soil surface. Metoxuron is used now regularly in the spring. With some fields in their sixteenth year of direct drilling it is not surprising that Mr Holbrook has found that broad-leaved weeds have also virtually disappeared, the reservoir in the surface soil having been exhausted.

Since 1975, Mr Holbrook has been conducting his own fertiliser and variety trials and has found he can achieve economic response from relatively high applications of nitrogen. He is growing quality wheat for a particular market and therefore uses growth regulators, mildewicides, fungicides and aphicides over his whole area.

The considerable increase in earthworm populations and their associated burrows, coupled with the extensive root systems of successive crops, appear to have added to the traditional drainage systems.

Mr Holbrook has found that direct drilling has greatly improved the 'load-bearing' capability of his land, that he is able to get on to his fields two to three weeks earlier in the spring than normal for top dressing; his spraying is never held up; he never suffers from combine wheel ruts.

The very high work-rate that can be achieved with direct drilling means that winter corn can be drilled at the optimum time.

Taken all round, Mr Holbrook has shown that direct drilling gives him the chance of carrying out all his farm operations when he wishes and when weather and ground conditions are exactly right. He can farm with nature, not despite it and, as an added bonus, since the whole farm has been direct drilled, his diesel fuel bill has been reduced by 75 per cent.

Mr Holbrook's yields over the years have been as follows:

Crop	1969	1976	1977	1978	1979	1980
		(tonne/ha)				
Winter Wheat	3·89	4·07	6·92	6·92	7·04	7·24
Spring Wheat	—	3·21	5·19	5·19	5·19	—

Equipment at Northey Farm
- 1 × 100 hp Crawler
- 1 × Beam Mole Plough
- 2 × 100 hp Leyland Tractors
- 2 × 4m Bettinson 3D Drills/Trailers
- 3 × 75 hp Ford Tractors
- 1 × Tasker Fertiliser Spreader
- 1 × 1545 Combine 13 ft cut
- 1 × 1530 Combine 12 ft cut
- 6 × 6 tonne Trailers
- 2 × 450 gall Trailer Sprayers
- 1 × Rotavator (5 ft)
- 3 × 175 cc Motor Cycles

Mr M Bendall, Manor Farm, Corston, Nr Bath, Avon[5]

Mr Mike Bendall farms a total area of 263 hectares, 235 hectares at Corston and 28 hectares at Keynsham. The soil at Corston is Cotswold brash, except for the low-lying areas which, like the Keynsham portion, are alluvial loams. Out of the total 93 hectares are in grass, all at Corston. Until a few years ago Mr Bendall ran a large dairy unit, but he has disposed of this and now brings in young beef animals, aiming at fattening on an 18 month—2 year system. For this he uses his grain, makes silage and supplements with home-grown barley.

In the dairying days Mr Bendall grew cereals, potatoes, grass and some kale, and he looked at direct drilling first in 1967 for drilling grass and kale, on a development basis, with the assistance of Mr Douglas Evans of ICI. First he used a Sisis Contravator (a machine based on a modified Rotavator, which rotated in a direction contrary to the direction of travel) to direct drill grass and kale seed, and was pleased with the reduced poaching which resulted, also with the rapid turn-round from crop to crop, and the savings in energy and labour which he achieved.

This led him to consider the possibility of direct drilling his winter wheat and in the autumn of 1970 he did this for the first time, using an ICI 'Fernhurst' prototype machine (based on a MF 732 frame) known as the 'Green Goddess'. Next he introduced direct drilled catch crop brassicae into his system following his earlier harvested cereals, and bought an International IH 6–2 cultivator drill to do the job. He has this machine still, and more recently he bought a MF 130 direct drill.

Mr Bendall now grows 70 hectares of winter wheat, 50 hectares of winter barley and 50 hectares of spring barley, all direct drilled. On the brash he produces a 'scratch-tilth' first wth a rigid-tine cultivator (having burnt the straw), then he direct drills. He feels the need to plough every 3–4 years to bury the stones. Standard stubble spray is paraquat at 0·7–3·0 l/ha, the rate depending on the stubble weed after harvest.

In some fields there is a sterile brome problem in the headlands. Cleavers are also a problem, and Mr Bendall uses a mixture of mecoprop and paraquat on those headlands to combat the two weeds. Blackgrass is present in quantity on some fields but chlortoluron applied post-emergence keeps this weed well in check. There is little couch grass on the farm; where it occurs it is dealt with by glyphosate.

Fertilisers
Winter barley receives 44 kg/ha N in early February, 44 kg/ha in early March and 88 kg/ha at the end of March or early in April.
Winter wheat—on the brash this crop receives a total of 176 kg/ha N split evenly between the end of March and the end of April.
On the lower lying alluvial land the total is reduced to 112 kg/ha again split evenly between late March and late April.

Yield

In 1980 the farm average yield of winter wheat was 8·40 tonne/ha.

Mike Bendall direct drills because it enables him to sow all his winter cereals on time. He aims to finish harvest in August, to drill the winter barley by 12–15 September and his winter wheat by early October. He shows big savings also in fuel and labour, and he believes his soil is better, more friable and freer draining even though the brash is ploughed every four years.

It must be said that it seems a pity to plough, which must surely destroy to some extent the continuity of pores and channels which is built up in the soil under a direct drilled regime.

High Mowthorpe Experimental Husbandry Farm, Nr Malton, N Yorkshire[2,9]

The soils on High Mowthorpe are silty loams over chalk, and are therefore, by definition, candidates for direct drilling and reduced cultivations, and yet their experimental work between 1971 and 1976 has led the ADAS staff there to the conclusion that cultivation systems at High Mowthorpe will continue for the time being to be based on the mouldboard plough.

Their experimental work produced the following information:

1. In first wheat crops following potatoes tined cultivation or direct drilling could produce grain yields equivalent to those achieved after ploughing. For second and subsequent wheat crops, however, tine cultivation reduced yield in four out of six crop years on average by 70 kg/ha, compared with ploughing. Further, direct drilling gave lower yields than ploughing in five out of six crop years, averaging 140 kg/ha loss in yield.
2. The depression in yield from very early (late September) or very late (late November) drilling of winter wheat has been greater from minimal cultivations and direct drilling than from ploughing.
3. High Mowthorpe's view is that the trash is more difficult to deal with under a reduced cultivation or direct drilling system.
5. Grass weeds, they say, are more likely to become a problem if a reduced cultivation or direct drilling system is undertaken for a number of years.

These points, which summarise the views of High Mowthorpe as expressed in their 1978 Annual Report, were also emphasised at an ADAS cultivation demonstration at Castle Howard in 1978, and the view was advanced there that there were many instances where farmers who had been practising reduced cultivation techniques for four or five years were now finding themselves with a serious grass weed problem. The point was made that such grass weeds were only controllable in the reduced cultivation regime if the job were done properly, otherwise the cure was an expensive herbicide programme. High Mowthorpe grow oilseed rape once in every five years, and they plough in crop residues before planting the rape.

Clearly, as has already been discussed, the practice of continuous direct drilling or 'no-plough' cultivations does demand very great vigilance with regard to the incidence of grass weeds, but one must be clear about one's objectives. The time-, labour- and fuel-saving aspects of direct drilling and reduced cultivations (particularly the former) are surely well established, so that the economics of the operation (savings versus money spent on herbicides), can be estimated in advance; admittedly these will vary with circumstances. It is beyond argument that a major virtue of minimal soil disturbance on many oils is the retention, via fissures, pores, and earthworm and root channels, of a good system for drainage and root penetration. It would seem a pity to destroy this once every five years, *provided* weeds and surface rutting do not become a problem.

True, yield disparities of the level mentioned by High Mowthorpe are not tolerable, and they are trying to find out why, on such a soil type, this disparity occurs. They are continuing with experiments comparing ploughing, shallow ploughing, tine cultivating, disc cultivating and direct drilling. In addition, they have two fields which are in continuous cereals, one tine-cultivated and one direct drilled, neither of which has been a total success due mainly to grass weeds and rutting (the latter as a result of combining in a wet harvest). High Mowthorpe make the following points as a result of their experience with direct drilling and reduced cultivations so far:

1. The period of the autumn during which direct drilling will lead to good yields is shorter than for ploughing.
2. The wetter summers, later harvest, and greener stubble of the North make a good burn very difficult to achieve.
3. The big increase in the area of autumn cereals has led to pressure for earlier drilling, reducing the interval between harvesting and drilling; this in turn allows less time for trash breakdown, and more opportunity for weed survival unless very careful and efficient weed control measures are practised.

Finally, High Mowthorpe are in touch with two farmer groups, one in North Humberside and one in Northumberland, who are pursuing minimal tillage with enthusiasm.

The foregoing case studies are merely a few examples illustrating farm systems based on 'no-plough' techniques; there are, of course, many more protagonists, and there are detractors. Whether or not these techniques are 'for him' must be worked out by every farmer for himself, but at least in 1981 there is some background evidence on which to come to a judgement. Table 41 sets out the areas of crops which it is estimated were direct drilled in the United Kingdom in 1980.

Table 41. Estimated areas of crops direct drilled in the United Kingdom, 1980

Crop	'000 hectares
Winter cereals	
• into stubbles	130
• into grass	6
Spring cereals	
• into stubbles	3
• into grass	1
Maincrop fodder brassicas into grass	
• kale and rape	18
• swedes and turnips	4
Catch crop fodder brassicas (kale, rape and turnips)	
• into stubbles	14
• into grass	6
Grass into grass	16
Grass into stubbles	23
Beans and peas	1
Maize	1
Oilseed rape	52
Fodder rye	2
Sugar beet	*
Other crops	*
*less than 500 ha	278 (approx)

1980 total direct drilling area divided into:
(1) contractor drilled   143,000
(2) farmer drilled   135,000
                                          278,000 hectares
(Source: Page, J N, ICI Plant Protection Division 1981)

The fact that winter cereals form such a high proportion of the total area of direct drilled crops is testimony to the strong motivation of cereal growers to use this technique for that crop. Note that only about 10 per cent of the total area of winter cereals is direct drilled, however. Cannell *et al.* estimated (see Chapter 4) that Category 1 soils cover 30 per cent of the cereal growing area and Category 2 soils a further 50 per cent, so there is plenty of scope for expansion of the system!

2. OILSEED RAPE

After a brief period of popularity in th 1960s, interest in this crop receded, but from 1970 onwards the area of the crop grown in England has increased steadily and fast. By 1980 92,000 hectares were grown (compared with 4,000 hectares in 1970) and the estimate for 1981 is 110,000 ha.

Oilseed rape can be profitable given a yield around 2·75 tonnes/ha; it may be drilled without recourse to specialised and expensive machinery and makes an excellent break crop in a mainly cereal rotation. Many farmers are achieving 3·5–3·75 t/ha, some, it is said, even 5–6 t/ha. Rape performs best on heavier soils which are able to retain moisture. Most of the oilseed rape grown is winter-sown; it is higher yielding than spring rape, has a higher oil content, and can fit very well into most farming systems especially where cereals are important.

Winter oilseed rape occupies the ground for ten months of the year—it must be drilled ideally in mid-late August, but certainly before mid-September, and is harvested in late July. It follows earlier-harvested cereals, usually winter barley, and because of the need for speedy planting, and because undisturbed soil will retain the needed moisture to get a crop away, direct drilling is an ideal system for sowing winter oilseed rape. This is confirmed by the fact that, out of 92,000 hectares of oilseed rape grown in the United Kingdom in 1980, 52,000 hectares were direct drilled.

The operation is simple and streamlined. If the straw is burnt, any remaining stubble weed should be killed by paraquat, and the rape direct drilled without delay. If there is no green vegetation present in the stubble, then burning alone may be sufficient to produce a clean seedbed. If the straw is baled, delay spraying until the stubble has greened up. Where the weed infestation is heavy it will be wise to wait for a few days between spraying and direct drilling. This will allow the sprayed weeds to collapse and will make direct drilling easier. Rate of paraquat will depend on the density and type of weed cover. In general practice 3 1/ha or even less is applied where the weeds are mostly seedlings, and 4 1/ha is used where the infestation is heavier and especially when creeping bent is present. The ICI label recommendation is 5·5 litres/ha to cover a wide range of weed situations.

Fortunately, the soil types on which oilseed rape is grown, mostly chalky boulder clays and other well-structured soils with a high clay content, suit direct drilling. But the 'golden rule' must be observed: avoid compacted and poorly drained soils. If the headlands are compacted, they should be broken up with a spring-tine cultivator first. Weedy fields, especially fields with rhizomatous grasses like couch and black bent, should be avoided.

FERTILISERS

The base (seedbed) dressing should be broadcast before direct drilling. Like all brassica crops, oilseed rape demands high levels of nutrient, particularly N, and a typical treatment would be as follows.

● *Winter Oilseed Rape*
In the seedbed: N—60 kg/ha; P—60 kg/ha; K—60 kg/ha.
As a top dressing: N—170-221 kg/ha.
● *Spring Oilseed Rape*
In the seedbed: N—60 kg/ha; P—42 kg/ha; K—42 kg/ha.
As a top dressing: N—102-153 kg/ha.

WEED CONTROL

Paraquat will deal with all weeds *which have emerged* before direct drilling. A typical weed control programme in winter oilseed rape is as follows: TCA pre-planting, for the control of grass weeds and 'volunteer' cereals (a most important weed problem in oilseed rape) followed by:

(a) 'Kerb' (propyzamide) in November to kill remaining grasses and broadleaved cereals;

or (b) 'Matrikerb' (propyzamide + 3,6-dichloropicolinic acid) in November where mayweeds are present *in addition* to grass weeds and 'volunteers'

or (c) 'Benazolox' (benazolin + 3,6-dichloropicolinic acid) in October/November where broadleaved weeds (*including* mayweeds) form the main problem;

or (d) 'Carbetamex' (carbetamide) for broadleaved weeds. For details of rates of application for these products consult the manufacturers.

A new herbicide is being developed by ICI specifically for use in rape. It is intended for early post-emergence application and will deal effectively with grass weeds, including wild oats, 'volunteer' cereals and meadow grasses. It will also suppress couch grass and will generally 'release' the crop from grass weed competition.

PESTS

As a general protective measure the rape seed should be dressed with HCH—this will deter the turnip flea beetle, but cabbage stem beetle, blossom weevil, pollen beetle and bladder pod midge are all potential enemies of the growing crop. HCH is effective against the cabbage stem pests and should be applied soon after crop emergence. There is some debate as to the most appropriate treatment against the pollen beetle in winter oilseed rape because it attacks at a time when bees are visiting the crop. Much depends on the level of infestation, but if treatment is essential, HCH sprays should be applied at early green bud stage, in early morning or late evening to reduce the hazard to the bees.

DISEASE

Phoma (stem canker) has increased in incidence and must be considered a major potential threat to the oilseed rape crop. It is most important to remove the rape trash and bury or burn it to avoid the risk of 'carry-over' infection.[4]

The following account illustrates how direct drilling can fit into a farm system involving cereals and oilseed rape.

CASE STUDY: A TWO-CROP SYSTEM FOR HEAVY LAND[6]

The Forsyth brothers together with a cousin, farm 582 hectares at Moorlands Farm, Kineton, in Warwickshire. The soil is Lower Lias (Evesham series) containing 45–70 per cent clay, all of which has been underdrained.

Two crops only are grown—winter wheat and oilseed rape (though there is a small area of winter barley on some rather lighter land)—and the Forsyths have worked towards a system of five winter wheats, an oilseed rape 'break' and then back into wheat.

The company also farm about 1000 hectares in the area around Kineton on a share-farming basis, and the work is carried out by their own family contracting company. They employ labour, up to thirty depending on the season, and with this labour and a range of machinery the contracting business carries out all the operations at

Moorlands Farm and on the shared farms.

The Forsyths first tried reduced cultivations in the very wet autumn of 1968, when they chisel-ploughed a field at Kineton and put in winter wheat. They liked what they saw, but worked towards shallower cultivations because, in their experience, once the soil is broken up, especially if it is on the wet side, it settles down more firmly than ever, and does not have the carrying capacity when in a moist state.

Direct drilling was introduced on a small scale in 1970 and worked well; since then the cropping system has been built around direct drilling and reduced cultivations, and they are now working on what they consider their target on Moorlands Farm of direct drilling 50 per cent of the total area each year. Good drainage is essential including regular subsoiling, and mole-ploughing every three–six years depending on the clay content. If poor surface soil structure is evident on a newly drained field, shallow-tine cultivations will take place for one or two years before direct drilling is introduced on that field. Needless to say, a good straw burn is an essential prelude to direct drilling on any field.

Forsyths believe that a flexible approach should be taken, depending on the condition of the soil at drilling time. Normally, a Bettinson triple-disc drill is used with chain harrows following; where the soil is free of trash, the front disc of each coulter is removed. On the other hand where necessary there may be a shallow-tine cultivation before or after drilling. The headlands require attention because they suffer the most traffic. Moreover, when combining, the grain is brought by the combines to the headland and emptied into tankers there; thus the headlands need breaking up with a cultivator.

The heavy soil at Kineton is stable and well structured. It is able to shrink and swell as it dries and re-wets, thus producing vertical cracks and fissures which help both drainage and root growth. Good frost tilth and high earthworm populations are also features of the soil at Moorlands Farm. These natural assets, which contribute towards quick crop establishment and satisfactory root development, need good husbandry, however, and the Forsyths are now sure that only by a system of direct drilling and reduced cultivations could they farm as they do.

Couch grass can be a problem in some years and direct drilling does nothing to lessen it; left alone, clumps of couch in fields continuously direct drilled could spread to unmanageable levels. These clumps are sprayed with glyphosate.

After oilseed rape, there is an opportunity for a type of bastard fallow before the next wheat crop, which provides a better opportunity to tackle couch grass.

Blackgrass is also a problem on certain areas of land, and the Forsyths have found that relying only on paraquat before direct drilling deals with clumps present but leaves the crop exposed to subsequent 'flushes'. In 1978, the winter wheat was drilled very early and sprayed with a mixture of isoproturon and bromoxynil/ioxynil/mecoprop esters. This was effective on both blackgrass and speedwell. A selective weedkiller is usually necessary in the spring to deal with cleavers.

Wild oats are an inherent problem. The overall burn, direct drilling and shallow cultivations, and the judicious use of chemicals has helped to reduce dramatically their significance although a watchful eye has to be kept on this problem to stop it reappearing.

Since 1978 blackgrass has reappeared. Dry autumns, and consequent poor autumn germination have resulted in many plants escaping pre-emergence herbicide treatment; moreover soil-acting herbicides have proved less effective because of the build-up of carbon on and near to the soil surface following stubble burning over the years. In consequence it has become necessary to encourage germination of the blackgrass by achieving a 'scratch tilth' before drilling and by using a foliar-acting post-emergence herbicide.

The carbon on the surface of the heavy soil has not proved evenly dispersible but has certainly helped to produce a 'kinder' and more workable soil surface. The Forsyths have found that their soils have worked more easily since they gave up ploughing and they are sure that this has contributed to higher yields. They have noted this also on previously ploughed heavy arable land which they have taken over and direct drilled for a number of years.

Yields have been very satisfactory; in 1978, 80 hectares of land growing Flanders winter wheat yielded 700 tonne of grain. On another field which has had eight successive crops of direct drilled winter wheat, the 1971 crop yielded 7·2 tonne/ha; around 1973–4 the yield was 4·3–5 tonne/ha, and in 1978 it was 6·2 tonne/ha.

REFERENCES

1. DAVIES, D. B., EAGLE, D and FINNEY, J. B. (1972), *Soil Management,* Chaps 5 & 13 (Farming Press, Ipswich).
2. DOVER, P. A. (1978), MAFF, ADAS, *High Mowthorpe EHF Ann. Rev.,* 1978.
3. OLIPHANT, J. M. (1978), MAFF, ADAS, *Drayton EHF Ann. Rep.,*

1978.
4. PAGE, J. N. (1981), ICI Plant Protection, personal communication.
5. BENDALL, M. (1981), Farmer: personal communication.
6. FORSYTH, A. (1981), Farmer: personal communication.
7. HOLBROOK, R. (1981), Farmer: personal communication.
8. JENKINSON, R. (1981), Farmer: personal communication.
9. PERKS, D. A. (1981), Farm director, High Mowthorpe EHF: personal communication.

Chapter 9
PRACTICAL GUIDELINES—
GRASS

The cost of renewing grassland nowadays is extremely high and there is constant debate and argument about the relative merits of renewal and renovation, that is, between reseeding and improvement. The discussion itself is outside the scope of this book. What *is* relevant is to consider the extent to which direct drilling and 'no-plough' cultivations can be of assistance to the livestock farmer, cattleman or sheep man, on lowland or on hill.

DIRECT DRILLING GRASS INTO GRASS

General
Direct reseeding of new grass seeds following destruction of the old sward is a feature mainly of intensive dairy or beef farms or of similar intensive units on mixed arable/livestock farms. Traditionally, this has been achieved by ploughing, discing, harrowing and rolling to provide a fine, firm seedbed, broadcasting fertiliser and either broadcasting or drilling the new seed mixture. The favoured time for the operation is governed by two main factors: the period when temporary loss of the sward is least important, and the likely incidence of rain. Spring sowing means losing the field until late June and carries the risk of spring drought, especially in the eastern part of the country; on the other hand, July/early August, on average, may be expected to be wetter and possibly the stocking of other fields may be more easily rearranged to compensate for the loss of the sward.

Clearly, techniques of renewal which dispense with ploughing are as much at risk of prolonged dry weather as is traditional re-seeding. Direct drilling, however, can offer two major attractions; first the whole process of renewal is more rapid and streamlined, and second, the consolidation of the surface is not affected so that directly the new seeds are sufficiently established cattle or sheep may be put in to graze.

Earlier chapters described and summarised a great deal of experimental work with direct drilling and reduced cultivation systems in cereal crops. In contrast, relatively few detailed experiments have been carried out in which direct drilling, reduced cultivation and traditional reseeding techniques have been compared in proper replicated experiments and carried through to measurements of relative productivity of swards established by the three methods. One reason for this may be that experiments involving livestock are more complicated than trials with arable crops. With the latter the yardstick of the direct benefit or otherwise of a particular treatment is the crop yield. With grass and other forage crops many factors intervene between the sowing operation and liveweight gain or milk yield. Hence sowing systems for grass tend to be studied on a whole-field basis rather than on small plots.

Guidelines for Direct Drilling Grass—Lowland Pastures and Leys
Main requirements are:

1. A well-prepared, fine and firm seedbed.
2. A well-drained, well-structured soil.
3. Good fertility.
4. Adequate moisture and warmth.
5. Suppression of pests, diseases and weeds.
6. Absence of 'toxic' factors.

1. *A well-prepared, fine and firm seed bed*
When direct drilling into reasonably open leys, provided the 'kill' is satisfactory, the Rotaseeder and the Moore Uni-Drill can produce such a seedbed. When direct drilling into older matted swards, the advice given later in this chapter should be followed.

2. *A well-drained, well-structured soil*
This is self-evident. To attempt to direct drill into an unsuitable soil will lead to poor root development and indifferent establishment.

3. *Good fertility*
With grass, as with any other crop, adequate amounts of major (and minor) plant nutrients are essential. When ploughing and cultivation precedes seeding the upper and lower surfaces of the top soil are well mixed within a 15–25 cm layer. With direct drilling, however, the grass seeds are placed in an undisturbed surface layer of soil wich in a run-down permanent pasture may well be deficient

in many of the elements needed. It is therefore essential to provide adequate N, P and K to enable the new seeds to establish and thrive (see later). A soil analysis will indicate requirements. Do not be miserly; ensure that there is adequate N to give the new seeds a good start. Bear in mind also that P requirement in particular may be high: 100 kg/ha or even more. Broadcast these fertilisers *before* drilling the grass seeds.

With lime, special attention will be necessary because the combination of leaching and the continual breakdown of surface organic matter is likely to produce an acid condition in the top 5cm layer of soil, where the direct drilled grass seed will be deposited. Thus a dressing of lime may be necessary in such situations before contemplating direct drilling.

4. *Adequate warmth and moisture*

There is nothing about direct drilling which is incompatible with these requirements; indeed, when moisture is limited there may well be a decided advantage in that the technique will minimise the soil disturbance, thereby reducing loss of surface soil moisture.

5. *Suppression of weeds, pests and diseases*

Diseases. These are not generally a serious problem, although in Scotland much of the grass seed is routinely treated with a fungicide before sale, chiefly as a protection against *Fusarium* spp. In any event, there is no evidence to indicate that a direct drilled crop will be more at risk of fungal disease than would a conventionally sown crop.

Weeds. There is no doubt that on soils of higher fertility the establishment of direct drilled grass seedlings can be threatened by invasion of meadow grasses (*Poa* spp), especially in the drilled slots. It has even been suggested that it would be better to direct drill the new grass into the sward *without* prior chemical desiccation, the argument being that the invasion of meadow grasses will be held in check by the old sward itself. Unfortunately, hard evidence on this point is lacking but it could be postulated that the old sward may also act as an effective check on the establishment of a new grass unless that sward has been suppressed first. Once the problem of invasion by *Poa* spp has occurred an effective selective herbicide (e.g. methabenzthiazuron or ethofumesate) would be the most successful solution, which of course adds to the cost of the renewal operation. Methabenzthiazuron at 1·2 kg/ha ai* will suppress *Poa* spp establishing in pure ryegrass swards. Ethofumesate, applied pre- or

* ai = active ingredient

early post-emergence at 1·5–2 kg/ha ai will suppress meadow grasses, blackgrass, bromes, volunteer cereals and chickweed selectively in direct-sown perennial or Italian rye-grass swards. Work at the Weed Research Organisation has demonstrated:

● that by selectively suppressing these weeds rye grass tillering is increased;

● that ethofumesate applied in the autumn may remain in the top 2cm of soil for at least five months, keeping fresh weeds at bay until the grass crop is tillered and provides its own protective canopy.

Research work in Northern Ireland is showing progress with breeding strains of perennial ryegrass (*Lolium perenne*) resistant to normal doses of paraquat; although one resistant strain has not proved persistent enough to be a commercial proposition, it is hoped that this work will be fruitful in the course of time.[1]

As far as other weeds are concerned, the hazards with direct drilled grass are no greater than with conventional drilling, provided any deep-rooted perennial broad-leaved weeds are dealt with previously, ideally in the season before the sward is renewed.

Pests—Insect pests can threaten a newly direct drilled grass crop, particularly leatherjackets and frit fly. When the old sward remains on the surface, leatherjackets feed there and transfer their attention to the new grass seedlings as they emerge. The direct drilled slots also provide the leatherjackets with a convenient pathway from one seedling to the next. Fortunately leatherjackets may be attacked effectively by mixing HCH leatherjacket pellets with the seed when direct drilling, which will at least reduce the risk of attack to the same level as that likely to be experienced in conventionally sown grass.

Frit fly is a more complicated problem. This pest (mainly *Oscinella frit* but other related species are also believed to be involved) is well known as a problem in spring on oats, and against this DDT proved very effective. Its occurrence in the autumn in the form of larvae of the third (overwintering) generation came to notice in the early 1970s. These larvae live in grass swards and can migrate from ploughed or sprayed grass to a direct reseed *or* to a following cereal crop. Frit fly attacks on emerging grass and winter wheat crop direct drilled into a chemically desiccated grass sward were quite common in 1974 and 1975, very infrequent in 1976, and particularly troublesome in 1977.[2] In the autumn of 1979 it became evident that newly established leys can be attacked not only by migrating larvae but also by a 'fly-in' of frit flies which lay their eggs in the new sward.[4]

It must be conceded that the frit fly problem, though certainly not confined to direct drilled grass, seems now to be sufficiently widespread as to offer some constraint against further rapid expansion of direct drilling of grass into grass. Since 1973 much time and thought has been given to possible methods of combating the pest, by the ADAS, ICI Plant Protection Division, and others. Two aspects of control have been considered, i.e. cultural control and chemical control. Regarding cultural control, the advice is to avoid September drilling: crops drilled in that month appear to have suffered most from frit fly attack. July and August sowings seem to be rather less at risk and attacks on April, May and June sowing are almost unheard of. If the farm is situated in an area where autumn frit fly attacks are common from year to year,the farmer may wish to consider direct drilling his grass in the spring.

Chemical control—Many insecticides have been tested against frit, and currently the Dow product based on chlorpyrifos is considered the most effective. In trials conducted in the autumn of 1980,[4] promising results were achieved with:
- a bendiocarb seed-treatment (Fisons), and
- chlorpyrifos mixed with the first of the split applications of paraquat on the old grass.

ICI's permethrin product, applied at emergence of the direct drilled grass, produced fair results but such a treatment would demand very precise timing.

6. *'Toxic' factors*
Work at Letcombe Laboratory (already described in Chapter 3) has indicated the deleterious effects that acetic acid liberated from decomposing straw may have on direct drilled cereals. To date there is no clear evidence as to whether a similar situation exists in the decomposing grass sward, but it is obvious that this point would repay further study.

Renewal of Lowland Swards by Direct Drilling

Ley Renewal
The first step must be to graze the ley tightly, leaving 5–7 cm of green growth. If the ley is cut before spraying rather than grazed, the sward must be allowed to green-up before the herbicide is applied.

Much depends upon the condition of the old ley. If it has been renewed when just past its peak to maintain a very high level of production in an intensive grass system, there will probably be few perennial broadleaved weeds present. With a long-term ley, couch grass and dock may have gained a foothold. If such weeds as docks are present in quantity they should be dealt with by asulam or mecoprop in the year before renewing. If this has been done then either paraquat or glyphosate may be used to kill the old sward prior to direct drilling; indeed glyphosate will have a direct effect on any perennials, grass or broadleaved weeds in the old sward. Paraquat may be used at any time of the season, but gives best results when applied in late summer (July/August) or early autumn when the grasses in the sward are past the peak of their vigour. 5·6l/ha of paraquat will normally suffice but if cocksfoot (*Dactylis glomerata*) is present in quantity or if spraying must be carried out in spring when the ryegrasses are growing vigorously, a split treatment of 5·6 l/ha followed ten days later by 2·8 l/ha is more effective. Glyphosate may be applied at 2·3 l/ha. If docks are present 3 l/ha will be needed and where docks *and* couch are present 4 l/ha will be necessary. Where a weedy long ley containing couch, docks, thistles, etc. is being renewed, 5 l/ha should be applied. For full effect against these deep-rooted perennials July or August is the best time for treatment.

Fertilisers
ICI Plant Protection Division's experience with *summer/autumn* direct drilling reseeds has led them to advise 88 kg N/ha, for three reasons:
● it improves the chance of an autumn grazing;
● vigorous seedlings are better able to withstand pest attack;
● Early root development resulting from an ample supply of N results in earlier growth in the following spring.
ICI's farm at Henley Manor, Crewkerne, Somerset use 88 kg N, 10 kg/ha P, 18 kg/ha K as a routine for autumn reseeds.

For *spring* reseeds following autumn kill of an old sward, 100–126 kg N/ha plus more N during the summer, will improve the chances of good establishment before the onset of winter.[4]

Having direct drilled the grass the benefits that should accrue are:
● that the whole operation, from killing the old sward to drilling the new seeds, has been speeded up, and
● that six to eight weeks after drilling, the new seeds, on firm, undisturbed soil, will be ready for cattle and sheep to graze.

Renewing Old Matted Lowland Pastures by Direct Drilling (colour plate 35)
Such pastures are likely to be *Agrostis*-dominant, matted, and of low fertility. If renewal by direct drilling is envisaged the following procedure should be followed:

1. It is probable that such a pasture, once earmarked for future improvement will need to be drained properly.
2. The sward should be grazed as tightly as possible in the autumn and any perennial broadleaved weeds should be killed as described earlier.
3. The sward should be killed with paraquat (use glyphosate if there is a substantial infestation of couch, blackbent or deep-rooted perennial broadleaved weeds).
4. Apply lime and slow-acting phosphate in the autumn.
5. Allow the winter to assist the action of the spray and the lime in breaking up the old matt.
6. Spray any regrowth in the spring with paraquat at 2·8 l/ha.
7. Broadcast N and K (no spring P is necessary if applied in the autumn).
8. Direct drill the new seeds when spring soil temperature begins to rise.
9. Roll to consolidate.

The same advice would apply to *any* pasture scheduled for renewal which is subject to winter flooding, because such flooding might well kill off a high proportion of the autumn-sown grass seedlings if they are not well established.

Alternatives to Complete Pasture Renewal
The expense of the total reseeding operation has encouraged investigation of alternative methods of improving pasture. It was discovered in New Zealand that, provided the level of perennial rye grass in white clover in a deteriorating sward was sufficient, weed grasses, especially Browntop bent (*Agrostis tenuis*) could be eliminated from the sward by first grazing tightly in autumn then spraying with very low doses of paraquat (0·7 l/ha); the ryegrass and clover would colonise the areas vacated by the killed browntop and the sward would thereby be upgraded. Experimentally it could be made to work but it required such a high degree of fine tuning that this technique, called pasture manipulation, was never adopted on a wide scale. The idea was also tested in the Republic of Ireland, but was never adopted commercially.

Another approach, which has made more headway, is known as

'stitching in'. This involves suppressing the growth of the old ley with a moderate to low rate of paraquat, such as 2·8 l/ha, and drilling 15 to 20 kg/ha of seed into the suppressed sward at say 25 cm row spacing, preferably with a Rotaseeder.

The WRO 'One-Pass' Technique

The Weed Research Organisation have designed a special drill to establish grasses and legumes in existing swards by what they have called the 'one-pass' technique[5] which aims at patching up mismanaged swards and introducing new species without destroying the existing sward by ploughing or overall spraying. WRO claim that the technique is designed 'to reduce competition from surrounding vegetation, remove trash and mat from the sowing line, place seed in an environment suitable for germination, provide nutrients essential for establishment and growth, and provide protection from predators, all in one pass.'

The technique involves three steps:

1. *Band spraying*, using a herbicide (paraquat, glyphosate or dalapon) in a 10 cm band with a spray pressure of 2·1 bar, and a low throughput nozzle mounted about 10 cm above the sward. Herbicide rates advised by WRO are:

paraquat . . . 5·6 litres per sprayed hectare,

dalapon . . . 9 kg per sprayed hectare.

2. The WRO machine cuts a mini-trench 1·25 cm wide and 1·25 cm deep in the centre of each spray band by two vertical offset discs and a skimmer which lifts the ribbon of turf and lays it to one side on the surface of the sward.

3. Seed and fertiliser are sown into the slot from separate hoppers operated by land wheels, and slug pellets are also sown in mixture with the seed. Row widths will vary according to the seed sown but examples are:

Italian ryegrass . . . 16·5 kg/ha at 20 cm spacing,

Perennial ryegrass . . . 13 kg/ha at 25 cm spacing,

White clover . . . 2·2 kg/ha at 35 cm spacing.

Messrs Gibbs of Bedfont manufacture a commercial model of this machine and the system is recommended for patching up poached or over-grazed areas, for introducing perennial ryegrass into worn-out leys or permanent pasture, for establishing legumes in all-grass swards, for 'topping up' permanent pasture with Italian ryegrass, and for direct drilling forage brassica crops. It is difficult to estimate how widespread has been the adoption of this WRO-developed technique. The welfare of improved species sown into worn-out permanent pastures with drainage problems would seem to be in question. On the other hand, the use of the one-pass technique to rejuvenate a ley past its peak but by no means worn out, may well be a very practical proposition.

Machinery for Direct Drilling Grass and Legume Seeds
The direct drills now commercially available in the United Kingdom have been described in Chapter 6. The large, versatile, combine direct drill, fitted with triple-disc coulters (e.g. Bettinson DD, MF 130) will drill a wide range of seeds including grasses and legumes. Bear in mind, however, that these are 'slit' seeding machines and work best where the old sward has been really tightly grazed or cut before drilling. Slit seeding in the presence of a quantity of sprayed trash may carry a risk of some of the herbicide on the trash being transferred to the emerging seedlings, i.e. 'the pick-up' effect; this risk is greater if the dead trash is thick and moist.

The Rotaseeder, which produces a 2·5 cm wide slot, creates a mini-tilth in which the seed can germinate and the risk of 'pick-up' may be discounted, though a tightly grazed or cut sward is still highly desirable as a matter of general principle.

The Moore Uni-Drill, designed like the Rotaseeder to drill at a 12 cm row spacing, though based on a disc, has also a hollow knife coulter. The disc is set at an angle, the knife coulter widens the slit made by the disc (i.e. produces a slot), the seed is deposited through the coulter, and the abrasive action of the coulter forms a mini seedbed in the slot. Behind each disc and coulter is mounted a Cambridge roller ring which firms down the soil in each slot. Each disc/coulter/ring unit is independently sprung so that the machine can follow contours (see also Chapter 6).

DIRECT DRILLING GRASS INTO STUBBLES

The conditions for successful direct drilling of grass into stubbles are exactly as for cereals. Obviously the grass should be drilled by early September at the latest to give an opportunity for its establishment and utilisation before the onset of winter. Direct drilling stubbles with grass and legume seed is replacing under-sowing on many farms, (a) because it is time saving, and (b) because it provides an opportunity for optimising cereal yields and grass establishment which does not happen invariably with under-sowing. It is also possible for the cereal grower to apply the optimum amount of fertiliser to his cereals without having to worry that in doing so he may run the risk of smothering his young grass seeds.

RENEWAL OF UPLAND SWARDS

Most upland grasses are susceptible to paraquat; so are some of the heaths. Ling (*Calluna vulgaris*) is susceptible to paraquat but *Erica* spp (the true heaths) are not. Fine-leaved fescues are better controlled if sprayed between September and December and flying bent (*Molinia*) before the end of July. Sedges (*Carex* spp) are moderately resistant.[3]

The undecayed mat characteristic of many upland swards can, however, pose a problem for grass seedlings. General experience with this aspect of direct drilling indicates that a more successful approach in many cases would be to direct drill forage brassica seeds, especially autumn stubble turnips, as pioneer crops, graze these down with sheep in the autumn and winter, repeat the operation the following year, and *then* direct drill grass in the late spring of the third year. Two years of sheep grazing improves fertility and breaks down the mat, providing excellent conditions for the successful establishment of grass in the third season. This has been extremely well demonstrated at Redesdale Experimental Husbandry Farm (ADAS) since 1974, and the work there is described in detail in Chapter 10.

Table 42. Areas of grass direct drilled in England and Wales 1966–80 (ha)

Operation	1966	1971	1973	Year 1977	1978	1979	1980
Grass into grass	240	7600	5,300	21,000	21,000	21,000	16,000
Grass into stubble			8,800	27,000	26,000	25,000	23,000

(Source: Page J. N., ICI Plant Protection Division, 1981)

Table 42 displays details of areas of grass direct drilled in England and Wales during the period 1966–80

REFERENCES

1. FAULKNER, J. S. (1976), *Proc. 1976 Brit. Crop Prot. Conf.* (Weeds).
2. Fox, H. M. (1978), ICI Plant Protection Division: personal communication.
3. HEDDLE, R. G. and YOUNG, C. D. (1964), *Proc. 7th B.W.C.C.,* 1964, 529–39.

4. HARRIS, G. A. (1981), I.C.I. Plant Protection Division: personal communication.
5. SQUIRES, N. R. W., HAGGAR, R. J. and ELLIOTT, J. G., *WRO Tech. Leaflet No. 2*.

Chapter 10
PRACTICAL GUIDELINES
—FORAGE CROPS

FORAGE BRASSICA CROPS

In the twenty years between 1950 and 1970 the area under fodder crops decreased steadily, and the 1970 figure was only one-third of that recorded in 1950. A number of factors contributed to this decline, in particular a decreasing labour force, changes in farm systems, weed control problems (linked with the reduction in available manual labour) and the advances made in growing and handling the grass crop during that period.[3] Fodder brassica crops suffered the same fate as Cinderella—they were neglected by all. Farmers lost interest in these labour-intensive crops; seed merchants had no enthusiasm for stocking, advertising or selling the seed, and until well into the 1960s little help came from the breeder or the engineer.

In the late 1960s, however, there was a resurgence of interest in the growing of fodder brassica crops. It is not possible to list the reasons for this in order of importance but there is no doubt that the advent of selective herbicides such as sodium monochloroacetate and desmetryne helped by providing a substitute for hand weeding. For kale, however, the major factor giving the crop a new lease of life was the development of direct drilling. Added to all this, in recent years breeders have produced significantly better varieties. The situation is now much improved compared with 1970 when only 60,000 hectares of kale were grown in England and Wales.[3] The official Agricultural Returns for the United Kingdom in 1979 indicated a total area of 261,000 hectares of forage crops for stock feeding (which includes beans, turnips, swedes, fodder beet and kale) of which 163,000 hectares were grown in England.

Maincrop Kale
Kale sown in midsummer for autumn feeding can make a valuable contribution to the fresh diet of dairy animals. For reasons of

PLATE 36
Foraging direct drilled kale in a wet autumn; NB comparatively clean animal. ICI Plant Protection Division

labour shortage, already mentioned, cutting and carting to the animals went out of favour. In situ feeding, on the other hand, resulted too often in cattle arriving in the milking parlour absolutely filthy, sometimes lame and with sore teats, having tramped around up to their udders in mud whilst feeding behind an electric fence in the field. In contrast, kale direct drilled into an undisturbed grass sward killed with paraquat provided a crop which could be fed off in the field with significantly less risk of poaching and puddling and with considerably less dirt being carried into the milking parlour (see plate 36).

Once demonstrated, the new technique found favour quickly and it was the first aspect of direct drilling to be adopted commercially. Within a very few years of its first commercial use in 1968 over half the kale crop in the South-West and South of England was direct drilled.

Very little experimental work was conducted with direct drilling of kale. The first kale experiment with paraquat in the United Kingdom was carried out by ICI at Jealott's Hill in 1963.[1] An Italian ryegrass ley was treated with 70 units of N per acre on 5

March 1963; all herbage was cut on 28 May (to represent early grazing) and three treatments were compared—see Table 43.

1. 2 lb per acre paraquat ion (i.e. 11·2 litres/ha of product) in 24 gallons of water was applied to the sward on 26 June and kale direct drilled in 7-inch rows on 27 June.
2. After similar paraquat treatment kale was direct drilled in 21-inch rows on 27 June.
3. The sward was ploughed on 4 June, cultivated on the 17th and 27th and kale drilled in 21-inch rows on 27 June.

Table 43. Fresh yields of marrow-stem kale (tons per acre)

Units N/acre	Sprayed/drilled 7-inch rows	Sprayed/drilled 21-inch rows	Ploughed cultivated & drilled 21-inch rows
0	7·1	8·5	16·0
100	20·5	22·0	23·6
150	24·1	24·2	24·0
200	26·7	26·8	24·3
S.E. (single sub plot) ± 0.6			

(Source: after Hood et al., Jealott's Hill, 1963) (Ref. 1)

The two important indications from these results were (a) the poor performance of direct drilling compared with traditional sown kale where *no* nitrogen was applied, and (b) the increasing response to increasing N by the direct drilling treatment, resulting in the superior yields at the highest N level.

In 1964 at 180 units per acre direct drilling and ploughing produced almost identical results, and in three trials in 1965 yields (at 200 units N per acre) were equivalent in one trial, in favour of ploughing in the second trial, and in favour of direct drilling in the third.

Another potent motivating factor leading to the rapid adoption of the direct drilling system for kale was the advent of the agricultural contractor specialising in direct drilling. In the South-West of England, with a pattern of small livestock farms, little in the way of machinery but with a renewed interest in growing a few acres of kale, the way was open for a contractor service. Contractors were equipped mainly with Howard Rotaseeders and Sisis Contravators (see Chapter 6) and trained by ICI Plant Protection Division in site selection and direct drilling kale. The technique mushroomed, to be followed by a similar burgeoning in the South and South-East. From a few thousand hectares in 1968 the area direct drilled had expanded to 20,000 hectares in 1972 and to 35,000 hectares by 1975.

The advantages of direct drilling kale into grass are as follows.

- A rapid turn-round from old sward to the seeding of the kale, so that the ley can be grazed to within 7–14 days of the time of drilling.
- Problems of midsummer ploughing and cultivation are avoided.
- Moisture is conserved in the soil surface at what is often a dry time of year.
- Few annual weeds are encouraged to germinate as the ground is virtually undisturbed.
- The ground remains firm, and when the animals graze the kale in the autumn they stay cleaner.
- There is better utilisation of the crop, because less of it is 'contaminated' by mud.
- If it is the practice to cut and cart the kale for indoor feeding, the firm soil surface maintained by direct drilling enables the crop to be harvested by single-chop forage harvesters. This allows maximum utilisation of the crop without producing deep ruts in the field. It gives also greater flexibility; in particular, it gives the dairy farmer the opportunity to move the kale area around the farm.

When selecting fields for direct drilling kale the same rules apply as for other crops; in particular the following points should be borne in mind.

1. Any deep-rooted perennial broadleaved weeds in the sward should be killed with an appropriate selective weedkiller, preferably in the year before direct drilling kale. Glyphosate will certainly deal with such weeds as well as killing the sward but its action is slower than that of paraquat and it is rather less suited to the 'quick turn-round approach' which this technique demands. This is why it is good practice to kill perennial weeds *well before* direct drilling is contemplated.

2. The field should be fertile and in good heart.

3. The site should be well drained, with good surface drainage also, and free from subsoil compaction and panning. If such a 'pan' exists it should be broken up by subsoiling at least 2–3 months before drilling.

4. Select a field which is reasonably level, with good access at gateways.

5. The sward should be open and trash-free. Trash shields the grass from the herbicide and may hold enough paraquat to be toxic to young brassica seedlings; these emerge very rapidly, especially

in warm moist weather and therefore they come into contact with the trash before the paraquat on it has been inactivated by sunlight. Cut the grass (or graze it) off, evenly and short (7–14 cm) and allow it to green up before spraying.

6. The ideal pH for kale is 6·0–7·0 and this should be achieved by liming, if necessary, in good time and well before spraying paraquat. Take a special note of the pH in the top 2·5 cm of soil.

7. If the kale is to be drilled early (before mid-June), it is best to apply paraquat as a split treatment: 4·2 litres/ha in 200 l/ha of water followed 7–10 days later by 3 l/ha. For later drillings (after mid-June) a single application of paraquat at 5·6 l/ha will normally suffice, but if cocksfoot is present in quantity use a split spray of 5·6 l/ha followed by 3 l/ha after a ten-day interval.

Glyphosate can be used effectively to destroy the sward but bear in mind that it does take rather longer to act and allow for this in the planning.

8. Drill the kale if possible when the ground is moist and friable and aim at a depth of 1·25–2·5 cm. Chain harrow or roll as soon as possible after drilling to preserve the precious soil moisture.

9. Protect against slugs—mix suitable slug pellets with the seed or broadcast them by hand or fertiliser distributor when damage is first noticed.

10. Kale requires generous applications of fertilisers, say 10–12 bags/ha of a 20.14.14 NPK compound (i.e. 100–120 kg N; 70–84 kg P; 70–84 kg K per hectare), broadcast at the time of drilling. Top dressing is recommended at 6 bags/acre of a 34·5% N compound i.e. 100 kg/ha N, or 6 bags/acre of a 25·16 NK fertiliser (75 kg/ha N plus 48 kg/ha K), the latter on potash-deficient soils.

There is some reason to believe that in the past two or three years the pendulum has swung just a little away from kale back towards late grazing of grass, but the area of kale direct drilled is still an important proportion of the total kale ara.

Direct drilling machinery for kale (see Chapter 6 for details)
The Rotaseeder is particularly suitable for kale, but the Moore Uni-Drill will do the job satisfactorily. Both machines produce a tilthy 'mini-seed bed'. The triple-disc drills (e.g. the Bettinson DD and the MF 130) will drill kale seed and, indeed, in the Midlands and the South-East of England most contractors use these drills for the purpose. The Gibbs Direct Drill, especially designed for brassica crops, has tines which cause considerable soil disturbance. More details of this machine are given in Chapter 6.

Choice of variety and type of kale
Marrow-stem kale is not very hardy and is grown mainly for autumn feeding; it should be utilised before Christmas, certainly by very early January.

It is usually sown in mid to late June.

Hybrid Varieties e.g. Maris Kestrel and Proteor are midway between Marrow-stem and Thousand-headed kales in terms of frost-hardiness. They are shorter stemmed and less liable to lodging than Marrow-stem kales and they are more digestible.

Thousand-headed kale. Yields are lower than with Marrow-stem and hybrids but the leaves and succulent side shoots provide excellent feed in late winter and early spring.

For detailed information about varieties consult NIAB Farmers' Leaflet No. 2 (1980).

Other Forage Brassica Crops

Main crop swedes and turnips
These root crops are well suited to the North and West of England and, of course, Scotland. In these areas yields of 35 tons per acre (88 tonne/ha) are quite common. They provide excellent winter feed and should be sown at the latest by the end of June, preferably earlier. Swedes *should not* be fed at more than 30 lb (12 kg) per head per day.

Dutch white turnips
Over the past few years Dutch white (stubble) turnips have become an extremely versatile forage crop. They are used now in the following ways:
1. As summer turnips.
2. As autumn turnips.
3. As catch crop turnips.
4. As a pioneer crop prior to reseeding on upland farms.

1. Summer turnips
These are sown after 21 April (to reduce the risk of bolting) and preferably before 10 May (to lessen the risk of drought). Grazing *must* start within nine weeks of drilling (assuming there is no delay in growth due to drought), even though at that time the crop may appear hardly ready. Failure to start feeding sufficiently early will result in too big a crop which cannot be utilised in time.

Direct drilling at this time of year is of great value as it retains soil moisture in a period of high evaporation.

There are two major advantages of summer turnips:
- They offer an abundance of feed in August when ryegrass production is at its seasonal lowest. This takes the pressure off grass and allows more silage to be made; also it makes reseeding easier to plan because more of the leys can be spared for that purpose.
- They provide a clean 'entry' for an autumn-sown ley or winter wheat, either of which can be direct drilled.

2. Autumn turnips
By the second week in July it is becoming too late to sow kale with any hope of a full yield. ICI consider it worthwhile for farmers to direct drill stubble turnips into grass at this stage. The crop grows rapidly and will be ready to graze before the kale—say in mid-September. This can complement autumn grazing of the leys.

3. Catch-crop turnips
In the Midlands and the South, and in some sheltered areas further North, there is enough time, warmth in the soil, and freedom from frost in the autumn and early winter to permit the growing of a fodder crop following earlier harvested winter cereals. In this way very good use may be made of land that otherwise would have remained vacant until the spring. Dutch white turnips may be used in this way and indeed have often provided excellent late autumn feeding. They do require an early *and dry* harvest so that they can be direct drilled in mid-July, when they may yield 40 tons (or even 50 tons) per acre (100–125 tonne/ha). Drilled in mid-August they may produce only 20 tons/acre (50 tonne/ha). Furthermore, a drop in soil temperature can play havoc with yield. Early August should be regarded as absolutely the latest time for direct drilling stubble turnips *as a catch crop*.

4. Dutch white turnips as a pioneer crop
This is described in detail at the end of the chapter.

Fertilisers for Dutch white turnips
As with kale, twelve bags per hectare of a 20.14.14 NPK fertiliser is the recommended rate, *all applied at drilling*. Top dressing is risky; applied too late it may lead to nitrate problems, bearing in mind that the turnips are ready for grazing 8–9 weeks after drilling.

Direct drilling
(a) Summer and autumn turnips into grass
The general guidelines for direct drilling are as already described

for kale. Sowing rate should be 2·25–4·5 kg/ha, the higher seed rate for later sowing. A row spacing of 25–35 cm is ideal for earlier sowing, but for drilling after the end of July i.e. for autumn turnips and catch-crop turnips, row spacing should be 13–25 cm. If the turnips are being grown for the bulbs, drill at 1·12–1·68 kg/ha at a row spacing of 25–35 cm.

(b) Catch-crop stubble turnips

Burn the cereal stubble after harvest; if stubbles are sufficiently clean no herbicides may be necessary. Glyphosate may be used if deep-rooted perennial weeds are in evidence but paraquat will cope with the weeds likely to be present. Guidelines for direct drilling catch-crop turnips are as for any other crop direct drilled into stubbles (see Chapter 8). The rate of paraquat will vary from 1·4–3 litre/ha in 200 litres water/hectare depending on the level of weed infestation. For details of rates of glyphosate see Chapter 8.

Fodder rape

Also a quick-growing brassica, it may be drilled as a catch crop after cereal. The earliest sowings produce the heaviest yields. If it is possible to sow in July it may produce 35–38 tonne/ha. The varieties Canard and Emerald (both with good mildew resistance) can achieve these yields. The variety Nevin is lower yielding and less resistant to mildew but more resistant to clubroot.

As regards direct drilling the same rules apply as for catch-crop stubble turnips (see above).

Details of seed rates, row widths and fertiliser treatment for the fodder brassica crops dealt with in the chapter are shown in Table 44.

Pest Control—Forage Brassica Crops

Slugs have already been mentioned—prophylactic treatment is always advisable when direct drilling brassica crops especially into grass, and suitable slug pellets should be drilled with the seed or broadcast, preferably by fertiliser spreader, very soon after drilling and certainly as soon as any sign of damage is apparent.

Triple-disc drills (with coulters at 36 cm spacing) enable the slug pellets to be broadcast through the alternate 'free' coulters as the seed is drilled.

Fleabeetles attack all brassica crops, both underground and after emergence of the seedling. An HCH seed treatment will protect

Table 44. Planting details—fodder brassica crops

| Crop | Seed rate kg/ha | Fertilisers | |
		Seedbed kg/ha	Top-dressing kg/ha
Kale	3·36–6·72	100–120 N 70–84 P 70–84 K	100 N
Swedes	1·00–1·68		85 N or 65N + 40K
Maincrop turnips	1·12–1·68	60 N 150 P 90 K	(potash deficient soils)
Dutch turnips	2.24–4.48	120 N 70 P 70 K	none
Rape	85	85 N 85 P 85 K	50 N

N.B. The *row width* for all these crops should be 25–37 cm.
(Source: Acknowledgement to ICI Agricultural and Plant Protection Divisions)

the seedlings up to the first true leaf state—later attacks should be dealt with by spraying HCH at the very first sign of damage.

Pigeons. In addition to the usual deterrents such as bird-scarers, dalapon at 3·4 kg/ha, applied when plants are between 2 and 6 leaf stage, will have some effect; such treatment will also suppress any grass regrowth which may threaten to compete with the growing crop.

MAIZE FOR SILAGE

Although it is over a decade since maize was first grown seriously in the United Kingdom there are still differing opinions as to its future. There are some, pessimistic about our 'typical English summers', who assert that the most northerly point in the United Kingdom where maize should be grown is the southern tip of the Isle of Wight! Its protagonists point to the value of maize as a high-energy winter feed, to the *fact* that it retains its optimum maturity for at least a month, to the *fact* that it is much easier to harvest in wet conditions than are most grass silage crops, and to the *fact* that in dry summers a good crop of maize may nonetheless be grown where grass growth may be very mediocre.

Forage maize fits into the dairy enterprise and if it is grown traditionally late winter or early spring ploughing is essential in order to allow sufficient weathering to make a good seedbed to be produced in time for a mid-April/mid-May drilling. If the crop is direct drilled it will go into grass, usually rye or Italian ryegrass, grown for spring grazing and cut for early silage, with only a seven-day interval between the last grazing and drilling the maize. Total seasonal production of grass and maize is thus maximised.

As with other crops, direct drilling maize can give it a good start in a firm seedbed and moisture is preserved for use by the germinating seed. This firm, undisturbed ground also makes harvesting easier especially if the autumn is wet.

The problem is that maize is a precision drilled crop, thus direct drilling requires suitable precision direct drills. ICI Plant Protection Division, in conjunction with Howard Rotavator Co. and Messrs Stanhay, produced such a drill but it is a very large machine, specialist in its application, and has not made much headway in a restricted market. The Gibbs Direct Drill is the only machine on the British market which is specifically recommended for direct drilling maize. It must be said that at the time of writing very little maize is direct drilled in the United Kingdom.

When drilling silage maize the objective should be a population of 108,000 to 132,000 plants/ha drilled at 5–7 cm depth. The row spacing should be selected to suit the forage harvester which will be used.

The guidelines for direct drilling maize into grass are those described for forage and brassica crops, but spraying technique is as follows (with paraquat):

First application—4 litre/ha paraquat in 200 l/ha of water at a spray pressure of at least 2 bars. Drill three days after spraying.

Second application (into grass)—four days after drilling and *before* the emergence of the maize. Spray with 3 l/ha paraquat plus 3·5 kg/ha atrazine in 200 l/ha *or*:

Second application (into forage rye)—before or after maize has emerged 3·5 kg atrazine in 200 l/ha of water. No second application of paraquat is necessary—in any event do not use paraquat after the maize has emerged, at least not as an overall spray.

Fertiliser requirements
Either 132 kg N, 66 kg P and 66 kg K/ha, all broadcast before drilling or, 22 kg N, 11 kg P, 11 kg K as a starter in the drill with the seed and the remainder having been broadcast before drilling.

Pests and diseases in maize
Fortunately maize is not prone to the foliar diseases of small grain
cereals. An HCH/thiram seed treatment is advisable and care
should be taken to protect seedlings against wireworm and leatherjackets especially when drilled into a killed grass sward. Again an
HCH spray will achieve this.

Other Crops

Rye for forage
The ideal time for sowing is August or early September, thus it
could follow early harvested winter barley. Guidelines for direct
drilling are the same as for winter wheat, barley or oats.

CASE STUDY: REDESDALE EXPERIMENTAL HUSBANDRY FARM

At Redesdale EHF, north of Otterburn in Northumberland, some
very exciting hill land improvement work has been carried out
during the past few years. Using new weapons—paraquat to
destroy the old *Nardus*-dominant hill sward, new UK and Continental varieties of quick-maturing turnips, and the triple-disc direct
drill—Redesdale have been improving their hill land over the past
few years by 'pioneer cropping' in the modern manner. Their
methods, costs and results were described by Mr Mervyn Davies in
the Redesdale EHF Annual Review for 1978.[2]

The Redesdale technique is a three-year operation, starting with
the application of magnesian limestone at 5 tonne/ha 9–12 months
before drilling the crop; this is necessary because the hill land there
is covered with acid peat of varying depths overlying clay. The area
to be drilled is grazed hard by cattle during the winter (sometimes
the herbage is 'topped' mechanically) to remove surface herbage
and open up the sward. The area is then fenced and two applications of paraquat are made (the first in autumn and the second the
following June) each of 4·2 l/ha.

The turnips are direct drilled with a triple-disc drill at 1·7 kg/ha,
mixed with mini-granular slug pellets at 5·6 kg/ha at least four days
after the second application of paraquat. At drilling time 500 kg/ha
of a 22.11.11 compound fertiliser plus 1 tonne per ha of Phosace
(21% P_2O_5) are broadcast.

Turnip varieties used include 'Civasto', 'Marco', 'Rekord', and
'Cyclon' from the Continent, and 'Imperial Green Globe' from the

United Kingdom. Redesdale have found that the faster growing, shallow-rooting Continental turnips cope better in the acid conditions to be found in the first year. Yields from first-year turnips were variable (20–30 tonne/ha of roots and tops) but second-year yields were higher and more consistent at 60–70 tonne/ha. Dry matter was on the low side at 8·7% for roots and 9·9% for tops.

Turnips fit well into the Redesdale sheep system. Lambs can be finished and sold on a rising market between November and January; lean cast ewes can be kept on to put on condition and sold profitably in December. Cross-bred and draft Blackface ewe flocks can be partially wintered on the turnips, thus reducing winter feed costs; furthermore, lambs can be moved from inbye land, allowing autumn grass to be kept for flushing and tupping the inbye breeding flocks.

The turnips are stocked heavily in 'breaks' so that the lambs taken from grass at the end of September are trained to clean up roots and tops. The 'breaks' are fenced with lightweight plastic 'flexi-net' fencing, which may have to be moved frequently under wet conditions, leading to high wastage of the small roots. Continental varieties (especially Dutch), tend to become woolly whereas British varieties seem to be better utilised. Careful selection of varieties, and direct drilling the selected turnips for *successional* grazing may be worthwhile.

Supplementary cereal/protein feed is of course necessary and total feed consumption per lamb on Redesdale is 25–30 kg plus about 2 kg of hay which is offered if there is no grass on which to run back.

Redesdale normally achieve 3,000 to 5,000 lamb grazing days per hectare from their turnips.

Lambs tend to go from grass to turnips at about 30 kg liveweight and gain from 3 to 5 kg per head after about ten weeks. They are drawn off for sale and should give an average carcass weight of 15 to 16 kg with a gross margin over feed and forage costs of about £1.00 per head.

To reseed to grass after two years of direct drilled turnips the land is chain harrowed in May and the grass seed broadcast by fertiliser spreader followed by a chain harrow. 5·7 hectares were sown in this manner in 1976 and 5·2 hectares in 1977. The 1976 grass gave 12,450 sheep-grazing days plus 690 cattle-grazing days from April to November inclusive 1977, equivalent to 503 livestock unit grazing days per hectare, similar to that obtained by inbye fields at Redesdale on mineral soils! The 1977 sown grass gave 10,700 sheep grazing days (214 livestock unit grazing days/ha) between August

PLATE 37
Lambs grazing first-year direct drilled 'Civasto' turnips at Redesdale E.H.F.
(many of the turnips have been uprooted).   ICI Plant Protection Division

PLATE 38
(*Foreground*) unimproved upland pasture; (*background*) first year of improvement programme: direct drilled turnips.   ICI Plant Protection Division

PLATE 39
Direct drilled ley following two years of direct drilled Dutch turnips as pioneer crops at Redesdale E.H.F.   ICI Plant Protection Division

and November 1977.

Redesdale EHF uses these enclosed areas as sheep grazing in conjunction with rough grazing. They can be used at peak demand period for flushing, tupping and lambing ewes; for grazing ewes suckling twin lambs; for grazing lean pregnant ewes before lambing; for overwintering hoggs; and for reducing stock pressure on inbye land from May to June, thereby releasing more land for hay and silage.

By this technique of improving selected areas of hill, productivity of hill land can be doubled fairly quickly and livestock output increased dramatically, provided stock rates and/or lambing percentages can be increased to match increased carrying capacity.

Total cost of establishing the ley in 1980 was £544/ha for the three-year operation (£313 and £110 per hectare for first- and second-year turnips, and £121/ha for 1980 grass), all of which qualifies for grant aid. These costs are soon recovered in extra output. This is a self-financing system with the majority of the costs recovered each year. The reseeds are remaining productive for far longer than was originally estimated, and the view is that, given correct management, they can be maintained indefinitely.

It is Redesdale's conclusion that this three-year reseeding technique is one which any farmer, large or small, can adopt without extra labour or machinery by using a contractor for liming, spraying and drilling. To quote Mr Jack Thompson, Redesdale's Director, 'I still believe that this is one of the most foolproof methods of reclaiming unploughable hill land, because very precise instructions regarding timing and rates of application can be given to the contractor and virtually no capital has to be laid out on expensive machinery.'[4]

REFERENCES

1. Hood, A. E. M., Jameson, H. R. and Cotterell, R. (1964), *Nature*, Lond., 4924, 14 March 1964, 1070–2.
2. Davies, M. H. (1978), *MAFF, ADAS. Ann. Rep. Redesdale EHF*, 1978, 40–7.
3. Toosey, R. D. (1972), *Profitable Fodder Cropping* (Farming Press, Ipswich), 1972.
4. Thompson, J. (1981), Director, Redesdale EHF: personal communication.

Chapter 11

PRACTICAL GUIDELINES —SUGAR BEET

There are two problems concerned with the growing of sugar beet that have stimulated interest in 'direct drilling'; the first is to do with seedbed preparation and the second with minimising the risk of 'blow'. Early attempts to grow sugar beet by direct drilling with a disc drill into unploughed land, at Gleadthorpe EHF, produced disappointing results—a modified 'one-pass' system tested in Norfolk has been more successful.

SEEDBED PREPARATION

The Norfolk Agricultural Station at Morley St Botolph, near Norwich, conducted an investigation in the years 1972 to 1974 into the problems of seedbed preparation for sugar beet. One result of this work showed that differences in time of ploughing in the previous autumn could affect seedbed preparation and subsequent establishment of the crop, largely because ploughing in December when the soil was wet resulted in a coarser tilth in the seedbed and poorer seedling emergence, compared with ploughing in September, when the soil was dry and friable. It was decided therefore to look at the possibility of avoiding ploughing altogether by developing a 'one-pass' system which would also permit more sugar beet to be drilled earlier in the spring into moist soil without compaction problems.[4]

A three-year experiment started in 1975 compared conventional mouldboard ploughing, chisel ploughing and 'no-tillage' as primary treatments, followed by various methods of seedbed preparation including strip tillage. We are concerned here with the work on strip tillage into undisturbed stubble; for this purpose a test rig was developed by the late Paul Koronka of ICI Plant Protection Division (see plate 40).

Following encouraging results in this series of three annual experiments, a long-term experiment was started on two sites. This

PLATE 40
ICI Test Rig used in strip-tillage experiments with sugar beet at the Norfolk
Agricultural Station.   Norfolk Agricultural Station

has compared cultivation systems over a rotation of sugar beet, cereal, cereal. In 1977, 1978 and 1980 one or other of the two sites has been cropped with sugar beet. Strip tillage into undisturbed stubble, using the ICI test rig, was compared with winter ploughing, followed by two passes of a Dutch harrow just before drilling. The test rig consists of a 'straight-blade' Rotavator set to cultivate bands 18 cm wide and 4–5 cm deep, leaving the remaining 32 cm between the rows undisturbed. A firming roller is set behind each Rotavator blade. In front of the Rotavator a tine 2 cm wide is set at 20 cm depth in the centre of each cultivated strip to loosen the soil at depth. This is a most important feature because it moves the soil where the tap roots of the beet will have to grow. Stanhay Mk 2 units are mounted behind the Rotavator so that rigid tine, Rotavator blade, firming roller and Stanhay unit are 'in line'. The machine drills five rows.

In 1977 and 1978 seed was drilled at 7.6 cm spacing and hand singled, but plant establishment (at 150,000 plants/ha before singling) was of a standard that would have made drilling to a stand a practical proposition.[6] In 1980 the trial was drilled to a stand at 19 cm spacing, but strip tillage was hampered by dead weeds and stubble blocking the drill coulters, which led to an 18 per cent reduction in plant population. This should be avoided in future by straw-burning and earlier over-winter herbicide spraying. Six nitrogen levels were included in the experiment. Table 45 indicates the yields of sugar resulting from the various treatments.[3]

In 1977 tine cultivations and strip tillage gave respectable yields, though strip tillage resulted in a 0.49 tonne/ha deficit of sugar compared with ploughing, at levels of N optimal for each treatment. In 1978 yields from strip tillage matched those from ploughing, again at optimal N rates.

In 1980 the drilling problems mentioned earlier, coupled with a dry May, resulted in a yield reduction following strip tillage, though again a reasonable sugar yield was achieved by this technique:

With *low* levels of N strip tillage gave lower yields than ploughing in all three years (see Table 45).

Table 45. Sugar yield in tonne/ha

Cultivation system for beet	Nitrogen rate (kg/ha)						
	0	40	80	120	160	200	Mean
1977							
Plough	6·83	7·38	7·94	8·24	7·96	7·89	7·71
Tines	5·76	7·10	7·54	7·69	7·87	7·91	7·31
Strip tillage	5·43	6·73	7·37	7·45	7·67	7·75	7·07
1978							
Plough	6·86	7·63	7·88	7·83	7·68	7·87	7·62
Tines	6·35	6·89	7·55	7·59	7·37	7·58	7·22
Strip tillage	6·59	7·41	7·78	7·70	7·93	7·93	7·56
1980 (provisional figures only)							
Plough	7·23	7·97	8·68	9·03	9·12	9·14	8·53
Tines	5·74	7·02	7·16	7·27	7·93	7·63	7·13
Strip tillage	5·52	6·30	7·83	7·81	8·22	7·43	7·19

The highest yields within each cultivation treatment are underlined
(Source: after Nuttall & McLean, Norfolk Agricultural Station. (Refs. 6 and 3).

There were no harvesting problems—indeed in wet conditions the firmer surface (inter-row) of strip-tilled beet made it possible to lift, whereas after ploughing and cultivation lifting was not feasible.

In spite of the disappointing results of the above experiments in 1980 there was encouragement from a trial conducted by the Norfolk Agricultural Station on sand land. In that trial strip tillage techniques were tested as a means of combating wind erosion. The beet was sown on 25 March and produced a crop with an average yield of 58 tonne/ha at 17.44% sugar.

Experience has shown that stubbles need to be free of grass weeds for strip tillage to stand a good chance of being successful. Spraying with paraquat or similar herbicides is essential in order to keep the stubble clean and weed-free over the winter.

The 1980 Annual Report of Norfolk Agricultural Station comments on the progress made by the station in developing the strip tillage technique and indicates that it is now (1980–1) studying simpler techniques for this method of cultivation, both at Morley and on very light soil in Suffolk, to combat wind erosion.[5]

DIRECT DRILLING TO REDUCE THE RISK OF 'BLOW'

The term 'wind erosion' calls to mind the American Dust Bowl of the 1930s and perhaps that was the most dramatic manifestation of what can happen as a result of excessive cultivation and general bad husbandry on unstable soils over a long period. Mercifully wind erosion on a grand scale is not a major United Kingdom problem, but the lighter sands and fen soils of EastAnglia are prone to 'blow' in the spring, and damage to sugar beet in particular can be very serious. Davies and colleagues dealt at some length with the problem in their book *Soil Management*;[1] they explained that 'blowing' starts with 'saltation' (jumping) of the smallest particles of soil which become airborne with gusts of wind and then fall back to the ground, their impact moving other similar sized and larger particles. The larger particles move along the soil surface ('avalanching') until stopped (e.g. by a ditch or hedge)—thus erosion removes the finer particles and leaves behind the coarser soil. Cropped land will offer some protection against wind erosion but a widely spaced crop like sugar beet offers no deterrent and can suffer in one or both of two ways: by direct loss of newly drilled seed which blows with the soil, and by damage to emerged seedlings by 'sand-blasting' from the blowing soil. Small plants may indeed be smothered by the blowing soil.

Various methods have been and are still employed to reduce wind erosion; two of the more common systems are strip cropping and inter-row cropping.

With strip cropping, strips of the row crop (sugar beet, carrots etc.) are alternated with strips of cereal such as barley. This is more common in the United States than in Britain.

Inter-row cropping, with occasional single or double rows of spring barley, is practised in East Anglia and the shelter strip may be killed with a herbicide when the beet is well established.

As the danger of 'blow' obviously increases with the number of cultivations carried out on these erosion-prone soils, the aim must be to keep cultivation to a minimum. For this reason, interest has developed in 'direct drilling' though the major development work on this technique has taken place in the Netherlands, where 10 per cent of the arable soils are liable to wind erosion.

The basis of the Dutch system is to carry out in the autumn all necessary cultivations to produce a level seedbed, free of ruts and wheel tracks, and rye is *broadcast* at 125 kg seed/ha, before mid-September. The necessary phosphate and potash are also applied in the autumn to reduce wheel traffic over the land in the spring. The rye is killed in spring with paraquat, normally at 4 1/ha of the commercial product in 600 1 of water, but if the rye is at G.S.5–7 (Feekes-Large) 5 l/ha is necessary. Spraying is carried out 3–5 days before drilling if the rye is a light crop but 4–5 *weeks* before drilling if the rye crop is heavy.

Drilling is carried out with a modified sugar beet drill with a disc coulter capable of drilling a slot through the dead rye mulch, a sharpened *drill* coulter which can make a furrow of the right shape and depth without smearing, and a press wheel to close the furrow after drilling without over-compacting the soil. Each drill unit must work independently and it may be necessary to put different weights on each unit to achieve the correct working depth. The drill is also fitted with spray tanks and a boom and nozzles, so that pre-emergence herbicides may be applied simultaneously with drilling. One such machine in use in the mid 1970s in the Netherlands was a Hassia drill.[2]

This rye mulch (direct drilling) technique has been tested in development trials, with reasonable success, but as yet the system is not in widespread use for British sugar beet. It has two disadvantages:

● an increased workload in the autumn, already a labour 'peak' for the arable farmer, and
● the danger that rye may suck moisture out of the beet seed bed in a dry spring.

The techniques of strip tillage and direct drilling under test by the Norfolk Agricultural Station avoid these two problems.[3]

REFERENCES

1. DAVIES, D. B., EAGLE, D. and FINNEY, J. B. (1972), *Soil Management* (Farming Press, Ipswich), 235–9.
2. LUMKES, L. H. and TE VELDE, A. (1974), *Proc. 12th B.W.C.C.*, 1974, 1073–9.

3. McLean, S. P. (1981), *Minimal Tillage for Tap-rooted Crops*, Paper to Power Farming Conf., Feb 1981.
4. Norfolk Agricultural Station (1977–8), *Ann. Rep.,* 1977–8, 16–18.
5. Norfolk Agricultural Station (1980), *Ann. Rep.,* 1980, 14–16.
6. Nuttall, M. (1979), *Brit. Sugar Beet Rev.*, **47**, 4, Winter 1979, 25–6.

Chapter 12
DIRECT DRILLING AND MINIMAL TILLAGE OVERSEAS

This book is concerned with the development of 'alternative' cultivations in the United Kingdom, and the source material for each chapter has been selected almost exclusively from research and development work carried out on British soils. Likewise, discussions about motivating factors for the adoption of direct drilling, and assessments of its economic benefits are related to United Kingdom farming. Direct drilling and minimal tillage systems have been developed in many overseas countries and are now adopted widely in commercial farming, but for different reasons. While economic factors and preservation of soil structure form powerful motivations for direct drilling in the United Kingdom, reduction of erosion risk and conservation of precious soil moisture tend to be dominant reasons overseas.

This chapter describes some of the more important developments abroad, and these are dealt with on a *crop* basis. For much of the information the author is indebted to Dr G. A. Watson, late of ICI Plant Protection who has reviewed the subject extensively.[11]

MAIZE

Only in the United States has direct drilling of maize developed to a major extent. Towards the end of the 1960s, Shear at Virginia Polytechnic,[8] published results of experiments with maize planted without cultivation, through trash in which weeds had been killed with a mixture of paraquat and atrazine. These results showed not only that maize could be so drilled successfully but that phosphate and potash, surface applied, could be taken up efficiently by the developing maize plants.

At that time farmers in Virginia and West Kentucky, farming on the slopes of the Appalachians, were under economic stress because they could only grow arable crops in the valley bottoms, leaving the erosion-prone slopes under unimproved pasture.

Shear's work paved the way to an alternative, i.e. cropping these slopes by direct drilling rye in the autumn, killing the rye and weeds with paraquat/atrazine mixtures in the spring and then direct drilling maize without disturbance of the soil and therefore without risk of erosion. Allis Chalmers adapted their corn planter as a direct drill and called it 'The No Till' Planter. Chevron, USA, embarked on a development/demonstration campaign with Allis Chalmers and, encouraged by a number of state research workers, such as Shear and Shirley Phillips (Lexington University, Kentucky), the technique developed rapidly.

In Continental Europe there has been little commercial direct drilling of maize. In New Zealand a minimal tillage approach has reduced from 4 – 6 weeks to 6 days the 'fallow' period necessary between cultivation of old pasture and the drilling of forage maize, the approach being to kill off the pasture with paraquat at 0·56 – 1·54 kg ion/ha. This 'spray/cultivate' system lends flexibility to the cropping programme and it is estimated that in North Island about 25,000 ha of forage maize are established annually using this method[6,7].

SOYA BEANS

Brazil grows a large and progressively increasing area of soya beans and has shown great interest in direct drilling and limited tillage techniques. The crop is grown principally in Parana and Rio Grande do Sul in rotation with wheat on erosion-prone volcanic soils. After forest clearance, pasture and coffee became the main crops and these in turn have been replaced by wheat and soya beans in rotation. Under conventional cultivations the erosion problem has reached mammoth proportions, and this has led farmers to turn to limited tillage.

The farmer faces difficult problems because soya beans are sown in high-rainfall, high-temperature conditions, which are also ideal for the growth of weeds, especially *Brachiaria plantagenense*, *Euphorbia geniculata*, *Digitaria sanguinalis*, *Aramanthus viridis* and many others.[9] If these weeds are allowed to develop in wheat stubble they make the sowing of soya beans well nigh impossible, and consequently minimal tillage techniques to suit the situation have been developed. In Parana, it is recommended that weeds in the wheat are kept in check with hormone-type weedkillers and after harvest the wheat straw should be chopped and spread as a mulch. Any significant weed emergence before drilling soya beans should be checked with a 'management' spray of paraquat at 0·2 –

0·6 kg/ha (or diquat if *Acanthospermum hispidum* or *Sida rhombi-folia* are problems). If *Ipomoea* or *Euphorbia* are present 0·5 – 1·0 kg/ha of 2,4D should be mixed with paraquat or diquat. In Rio Grande do Sul (Southern Brazil) an initial 'stressing' spray of 0·2 kg/ha each of paraquat and diquat is followed 5–7 days later by a tank mix of 0·2 kg paraquat, 0·2 kg diquat and 0·7 kg metribuzin per hectare.[1]

Sowing of the crop at present is achieved with the 'Rotocaster', a modified rotary cultivator. As the direct drilling technique does not permit the incorporation of residual herbicides, severe weed infestations develop, especially of *Euphorbia geniculata* and *Sida*, and inter-row weeding units have been developed to cope with such weeds by directed application of paraquat and diquat.

55,000 ha of soya beans were direct drilled in these two Brazilian states both in 1977 and 1978, and use of the technique is spreading; studies with the technique are also in progress in rotations of cotton and maize as well as soya beans with winter wheat.

SMALL-GRAIN CEREALS

Direct drilling of small grain cereals assisted by the use of paraquat has made most headway outside the United Kingdom in Brazil (see above), Australia and to a lesser extent in New Zealand. In Continental Europe, though considerable research with limited tillage techniques has been carried out (in Holland, Czechoslovakia, Germany—where straw-burning is forbidden by law—France and Yugoslavia) relatively little commercial development has taken place as yet.

In Australia the reasons for direct drilling small grains are different from those obtaining in the United Kingdom. Cereals are grown extensively, on large farms with the minimum of labour available, on erosion-prone soil, with rainfall seasonal and at times heavy during the sowing period, yet scarce overall. The predominant agricultural system in temperate Australia is a wheat/pasture rotation. In Western Australia in the wheat belt, pastures regenerate each year from seed set in the previous autumn and are based on subterranean clover (and in drier areas *Medicago* spp.) together with Wimmera ryegrass (*Lolium rigidum*), barley grass (*Hordeum leporinum*), silver grass (*Vulpia* spp.), soft brome (*Bromus mollis*), ripgut (*Bromus rigidum*), capeweed (*Arctotheca calendula*) and *Erodium* spp.

The traditional cultivation for cereals involves disc ploughing followed by a number of cultivations. 'Spray-seed', which is replacing this, involves tight grazing of the sward then application of 2 litres/ha of a mixture of 125g paraquat plus 75g diquat per litre followed after 4–5 days by a one-pass cultivating and seeding operation.

Classical direct drilling with triple-disc drills involving absolutely minimal disturbance of the soil is now under wide-scale development, but Wimmera ryegrass is a severe problem. This grass can be controlled by the pre-planting incorporation of trifluralin, but the cultivation required to achieve this causes loss of valuable moisture. On the other hand, direct drilling assisted by paraquat helps to conserve moisture, but does not cope with Wimmera ryegrass which has not germinated at the time of spraying. The seed production of this grass can be reduced by the use of the 'Spray-top' technique, spraying the pasture with 20% paraquat solution at seed set. It is very possible that a combination of tight grazing, 'Spray-top', 'Spray-seed', direct drilling with a triple-disc drill, and the post-planting use of diclofop methyl will give useful control of Wimmera ryegrass and conserve moisture as well, leading to a satisfactory establishment of wheat.

55,000 ha of wheat were sown using 'Spray-seed' in 1977 in Western Australia and 15,000 ha in South Australia. By 1980 the total area to be planted by this method throughout Australia was 330,000 hectares.

In New Zealand on more fertile soils growing good grass, in conventional practice the pasture/cereal rotation demands a fallow period of some weeks between the breaking up of the old sward and sowing wheat to allow decomposition of the thick turf, which requirement necessarily limits flexibility. O'Connor & Mackay,[6] and others have shown that the fallow period can be shortened significantly by using paraquat, alone or in mixture with dicamba, as a pre-cultivation spray on the old sward, without any adverse effect of the establishment of cereal.

FORAGE CROPS

In New Zealand, kale (called chou-moellier) is direct drilled into pasture on a commercial scale.

The pasture is usually sprayed with a mixture of paraquat (at 1·12 kg/ha) and dicamba (at 0·42 kg/ha) to suppress white clover. In Southland (New Zealand) an alternative approach is to direct drill forage oats into pasture to increase summer food supply, providing dry matter yields of up to 12,000 kg/ha.[5]

GRASSLAND

In New Zealand the technique of pasture manipulation using paraquat was developed. In this method paraquat is applied at 0·15 kg/ha in late spring or early summer to a tightly grazed sward (which must contain enough ryegrass to be an 'improvable' proposition) to control weeds, suppress bent (*Agrostis* spp.), encourage clover growth in their place and permit the recovery and expansion of the ryegrass component in the autumn. The technique is inexpensive but requires fine-tuning and considerable skill in its implementation, and in spite of its obvious attraction it is not used widely.

One particular use of pasture manipulation with paraquat in New Zealand is to suppress barley grass (*Hordeum leporinum*) pasture, because the seed head of this grass can be damaging to grazing sheep. Paraquat has limitations, however, because it suppresses not only barley grass but desirable grasses also, and other herbicides have been tested, such as propyzamide, carbetamide, ethofumesate and dalapon with varying degress of success.

In Japan, on the northern island of Hokkaido, where half of the agricultural area is under grass, the Prefectural Government plans to increase numbers of beef and dairy cattle over the next decade. In order to keep within bounds their import bill for animal feeds they are seeking to improve their pastures. They are convinced that more frequent renewal of grassland is necessary; renewal by ploughing, cultivating and reseeding is a very expensive operation and they are investigating the feasibility of renewal by direct drilling. The soils of Southern and Eastern Hokkaido are basically volcanic ash so in theory they offer possibilities for direct drilling and full-scale trials are now in progress.[10]

RICE

Limited tillage techniques, assisted by paraquat, have also been developed in a number of other crops around the world, particularly in rice. In Japan, for example, traditionally rice is a labour-intensive crop. The rice growing areas lie fallow over winter, are ploughed in January/February, tilled two or three times in April and May with a rotary cultivator followed by puddling, levelling and transplanting in May/June.

With the help of paraquat a system has been developed which eliminates the need for winter ploughing (an operation performed mainly for the purpose of controlling annual weeds). It involves applying paraquat to the rice areas about four weeks before spring cultivation i.e. before the weed growth is too dense, and to ensure that the weeds will have started to decompose before cultivation.[2] Elimination of weeds is also an important factor in pest management; for example *Alopecurus aequalis*, a major weed grass, is a host plant of the green planthopper (*Nephotettix cincticeps*), an important vector of 'dwarf' or 'stunt' virus.

Paraquat treatment will kill *Alopecurus* before it runs to seed, thus reducing significantly the amount of seed carried forward to the next season.

Paraquat-assisted minimal tillage techniques have also been developed in S.E. Asia especially in Malaysia, where dalapon (at 1·68 kg/ha) followed three days later by paraquat at 0·56 kg/ha have produced complete control of ratooning rice and grass spp. in direct drilling trials. The sprays are followed by flooding and transplanting. When necessary MCPA may be mixed with paraquat in order to broaden the spectrum of weed control.

More recent work in the Philippines showed that glyphosate followed by paraquat (rather than tank mixes of these chemicals) give a very broad spectrum of weed control.[3,4]

General conclusions from work in the Far East are that preplanting weed control, using paraquat and other appropriate herbicides, must be combined with one cultivation and several days of complete flooding for optimum results to be obtained.

In Colombia and in Brazil, the 'stale seedbed' technique is used for the control of red rice. The seedbed is first prepared normally, then the land is flooded and the red rice allowed to germinate; the seedlings are then sprayed with paraquat from ground or air and the rice crop is sown either aerially or with drills producing minimal disturbance of the seedbed.

REFERENCES

1. BARKER, M. R. and WÜNSCHE, W. A. (1977), *Outl. Agric.*, **9** (3), 114–20.
2. BROWN, I. A. and QUANTRILL, R. A. (1973), *Outl. Agric.*, **7** (4), 179–83.
3. DATTA, S. K. DE., BOLKEN, F. R. and LIL, W. R. (1977), *8th Ann. Conf. Pest Cont. Council*, Philippines, 1977, 1–16.
4. ELIAS, R. S. (1969), *Outl. Agric.*, **6** (2), 67–70.
5. HAY, R. J. H., and RYAN, D. L. (1977), *Proc. Int. Conf. Energy Conservation in Crop Prod.* (Massey Univ., N. Z.,) 1977, 79–82.
6. O'CONNOR, B. P. and McKAY, A. G. (1977), *Proc. Int. Conf. Energy Conserv. in Crop Prod.* (Massey Univ., N. Z.) 1977, 58–62.

7. PALMER, P. C., O'CONNOR, B. P. and McKAY, A. G. (1974), *Proc. 12th B.W.C.C.,* 1974, 329–86.

8. SHEAR, G. M. and MOSCHLER, W. W. (1969), *Agronomy,* **61**, 524–6.

9. WILES, T. L. (1976), *Proc. Congr. Latin Amer. Weed Soc.,* Mar del Plata, 1976.

10. ALLEN, H. P. (1979 & 1980). Unpublished Reports (ICI Plant Protection Division).

11. WATSON, G. A. (1981). Monograph 'Weed Control in Limited Tillage', Weed Sci. Soc. America. (In Press).

Chapter 13
SOME FINAL REFLECTIONS

The emphasis throughout this book has been on minimal tillage (in the main on direct drilling) as an alternative to ploughing. There are other cultivation systems, however, in which the mouldboard plough has no place but which by no stretch of the imagination can be called 'minimal tillage', which are practised in situations in which, at least initially, direct drilling would not be practical. Two examples of such systems are to be found in Essex on the Dengie peninsula between the estuaries of the rivers Blackwater and Crouch.

Mr John Muirhead farms 280 hectares at Bradwell-on-Sea. On the higher ground his soils are silt loams and on the lower ground there are areas of silty clay loams/silty clays. His major enterprise is cereals and his main break crops are peas, lucerne and grass grown for seed. Mr Muirhead's conviction is that such soils must be loosened from the top, leaving a firm but not too cloddy seedbed. He aims also to 'capture' as much water as possible, (but to get the excess moisture away from the soil surface), and most of all to encourage the proliferation of roots at depth so that they may tap the reserves of moisture in early summer.

Mr Muirhead started with PTO-driven subsoilers but they proved unreliable, and eventually he constructed his own cultivator which he has named the 'Progressive' Cultivator (see photograph). The machine has seven leading sweep-tines, seven mid-depth tines and two deeper subsoiling tines at the rear. It is used post-harvest, when the land can bear the heavy tackle, and the depth of working is determined by the moisture content of the soil, i.e. as deep as 56 cm following a dry summer and limited to 38 cm when the soil is wetter. The cultivator is drawn by a large tractor equipped with double rear wheels.[3,4]

From time to time these deep cultivations have smashed some of the long-established pipe drains, but Mr Muirhead's contention is that his deep subsoiling and soil loosening is coping with the drain-

PLATE 41
Mr. John Muirhead's Progressive (original) Cultivator.   Farmers Weekly

age requirements adequately—in fact his view is that if the drains are running, precious water is being wasted: in an area with an average annual rainfall of only 530 mm (21 in) he may well have a point! His overall yields of winter wheat have been not far short of 10 tonne/ha (4 tons/acre) for the past three years with a 21 ha (52 acres) field yielding 11·2 tonne/ha (nearly 4½ tons/acre) in 1977. In discussion the author suggested that if the continuous pore system provided by his deep cultivations were stable, direct drilling might be feasible; the essence of Mr Muirhead's reply was that on his soils he considered that annual subsoiling is a prerequisite for continued high cereal yields.

Between Bradwell-on-Sea and Burnham-on-Crouch, Strutt & Parker Farms Ltd farm 1875 ha of marshland in six farm groups. Most of the soils are derived from heavy estuarine alluvium, mostly of the Wallasea series with some classified as Agney. The Wallasea soils are mostly heavy silty clay loams or silty clays (heavier than John Muirhead's); they are non-calcareous and suffer from wetness problems due to the combined effects of poor drainage and ground water. Some of the soils have a high content of sodium deposited from sea water flooding into subterranean creeks and six years ago carried a very poor vegetation of low quality native grasses.[6,8]

Application of sugar beet factory waste rich in lime is achieving a successful reduction of sodium (by base exchange, calcium for sodium) and in 1981 fields which were agriculturally useless are now supporting very creditable crops of winter wheat and barley.

Like John Muirhead, Strutt & Parker Farms believe that the soil must be loosened from the top and they have constructed their own version of the 'Progressive' cultivator, with three sets of tines which may be operated at three different levels or at one level, as required. This implement is pulled with an enormous Ford FW30 tractor with four double wheels, yet exerting a ground pressure of only about 7 lb per sq in! At a cost of around £40,000 it is not for the small man but for a large farming enterprise like Strutt & Parker Farms Ltd it is a means —and they believe the only means—of bringing their heavy low lying clays into farming.

The above examples illustrate the art of 'making' a soil, virtually from scratch and they represent a very special way of improving land capability; they are not to be confused with the use of highly powered equipment to produce a tilth by force, which could be defined as agricultural rape! Most of the book is about *conserving* soils but direct drilling can also 'make' as well as conserve soil structure providing certain prerequisites are met.

We are now twenty years on from the first chemically assisted direct drilling experiments in the United Kingdom, and the technique, with its variations, has come to stay. What of its future—how, and in what directions will it develop? Quite obviously there will be many and differing views on this topic.

In the author's opinion there are two major hurdles to clear if the practice of planting crops following minimal tillage is to expand substantially. First, it must be considered as a *farm system*, and its potential advantages and limitations must be researched very thoroughly before it is attempted. Second, the development of minimal tillage practices must be accompanied by a fundamental change of thinking about the loads which we impose upon our long-suffering soils at sowing, when applying fertilisers and sprays, and at harvest. Much has been written and spoken on this theme by Elliott,[1,2] Soane,[7] and many others. Pidgeon[5] has considered the ultimate in minimal tillage, i.e. broadcasting cereal seed on to uncultivated soil following spraying with glyphosate to control weeds, particularly couch grass.

The case for a combined approach by agronomists, soil scientists, machinery, vehicle and tyre manufacturers to produce a low-pressure 'package' to accompany direct drilling is overwhelming, if our concern about soil care is really as deep as public utterances suggest.

REFERENCES

1. ELLIOTT, J. G., *A.R.C. Rev.*, **4** (3), 76–8.
2. ELLIOTT, J. G., *S.A.W.M.A. Conf., Soil Compaction and Cures*, Silsoe, Feb. 1981.
3. HOPE, H., *Farmers' Weekly*, 7 July 1978, vii.
4. MUIRHEAD, J., Farmer, Essex: personal communication.
5. PIDGEON, J. D., *Prelim. Study Min. Till. Systems* (inc. broadcasting) for spring barley in Scotland.
6. PIZER, N. F., Consultant: personal communication.
7. SOANE, B. D., *S.A.W.M.A. Conf. Soil Compaction and Cures*, Silsoe, Feb. 1981.
8. WOODHEAD, A., Farmer, Essex: personal communication.

DOUBLE CONVERSION TABLES

Pints per Acre/Litres per Hectare

Pints per Acre		Litres per Hectare
0·71	1	1·40
1·42	2	2·80
2·13	3	4·20
2·84	4	5·60
3·55	5	7·00
4·26	6	8·40
4·97	7	9·80
5·68	8	11·20

Gallons per Acre/Litres per Hectare

Gallons per Acre		Litres per Hectare
0·892	10	112·08
1·784	20	224·17
2·676	30	336·25
3·569	40	448·34
4·456	50	560·43
5·353	60	672·51
6·245	70	484·56
7·137	80	896·68
8·029	90	1008·77
8·922	100	1120·85

N.B. To convert pints per acre into litres per hectare multiply by 1·40; to convert litres per hectare into pints per acre multiply by 0·71.

Pounds per Acre/Kilogrammes per Hectare

Pounds per Acre		Kilogrammes per Hectare
0·892	1	1·121
1·784	2	2·242
2·677	3	3·363
3·569	4	4·483
4·461	5	5·604
5·353	6	6·725
6·245	7	7·846
7·137	8	8·967
8·030	9	10·088
8·922	10	11·209
17·844	20	22·417
26·765	30	33·626
35·687	40	44·834
44·609	50	56·043
53·331	60	67·251
62·453	70	78·460
71·374	80	89·668
80·296	90	100·877
89·218	100	112·085
133·827	150	168·128
178·436	200	224·170
223·045	250	280·213
267·654	300	336·255

N.B. To convert lb/acre to kg/ha multiply by 1·12, to convert kg/ha into lb/acre multiply by 0·892

INDEX

213